THE BEST WINES IN THE SUPERMARKETS 2019

NED HALLEY

foulsham
LONDON • NEW YORK • TORONTO • SYDNEY

W. Foulsham & Co. Ltd
for Foulsham Publishing Ltd
The Old Barrel Store, Drayman's Lane, Marlow, Bucks SL7 2FF

Foulsham books can be found in all good bookshops and direct from www.foulsham.com

ISBN: 978-0-572-04746-7

A CIP record for this book is available from the British Library

Printed and bound in Great Britain by Martins the Printers Ltd

Contents

—*All's well with wine*—

Good news. In spite of apocalyptic weather events in the vineyards and heightening alarm over Brexit, there is no shortage of wines from Europe – or anywhere else – in the supermarkets.

More good news. In spite of the collapse of the pound, especially against the euro, and the endless hiking of UK excise duty on alcohol, wine prices in the supermarkets have scarcely increased at all since last year.

Is the wine trade immune to market forces? Well, no. Wine in Britain is now in what is called a mature market. Demand has peaked. We are now officially a wine-drinking nation. We're enjoying better and better wines in gradually reducing quantities as we get pickier in our tastes and more heedful of the need for moderation.

Well, maybe. What is certain is that our overall alcohol consumption is in gentle decline, and wine has long since overtaken beer as the preferred beverage at home. And the supermarkets are on to it.

The trend towards own-label wines continues. As supermarkets strive to distinguish their offerings from those of their rivals, house wines are becoming a major force in the brand wars. I am often asked which supermarket has the best wine? I am flummoxed for an answer, but am conditioned to reply that Sainsbury's Taste the Difference can definitely be counted on, but so can Tesco's Finest, and so can Asda's Extra Special – and so on.

Whichever supermarket you happen to find yourself in, you should be able to find a decent bottle of wine at a sensible price. The only problem is that there tends to be far too much choice. If you're sufficiently interested in wine to have bought this book and read this far, you won't be solving the problem by just picking up a bottle of Blossom Hill.

The Best Wines in the Supermarkets works on the premise that you've already made your choice of supermarket. It's the wine you're not so sure about. So the book is divided up into sections under the headings of the retailers who have the best ranges. Within each section I list the wines according to countries of origin because this is still pretty much how the supermarkets do it in their stores.

In describing each wine, I'm trying to delineate its style and why it deserves a mention. My scoring system is based on the points I note at the time of tasting, from 0 to 10. Over the year preceding the completion of the book I taste thousands of wines, but there's room for only about 500 in this pocket-sized format (don't leave home without it) so there's space only for the pick of the bunch. Very few wines mentioned have scored under 8, signifying I've liked them a lot and think them good value. The scores are very definitely value-linked. During the last year I have tasted supermarket wines costing up to and beyond £100 a bottle, and a few of these have been terrifically good. But the most expensive wine I have recommended this year is priced at £29.99 – and I fear I might have included it for facetious reasons.

So, value is a big factor. A wine scoring 9 in these pages is always exceptionally good, interesting and fair value. Wines scoring 10 are those I believe to be unrivalled in their class. That there are 30 of these this year is testament either to the general excellence of supermarket wines or to my Panglossian enthusiasm.

The few wines you'll find below 8 points are those I have very much liked but fear are overpriced or underaged. I've awarded one wine a big, fat 0 – again I fear, for facetious reasons.

I do try to keep a sense of proportion in writing about all these wines. This branch of journalism, if I can call it that, can be a little too earnest, so if I do digress from time to time I hope you will indulge me. And in the age of social media, wine writers no longer enjoy the monopoly we once did. Now, I can compare my own notes not just with those of the retailers, but with those of their online customers.

Here is a Lincolnshire lady's opinion of an expensive M&S Italian red I thought was 'sleek and plump'. 'This wine has no taste', she averred. 'Nothing else to say other [than] don't waste your money'. M&S's own description: 'Full-bodied yet elegant with blackberry, cherry and dried flower notes over a smooth, delicately spiced palate'. Brilliant! Another lady summarises Tesco Mâcon-Villages Blanc: 'Only one word to describe this ... Ghastly. Best avoid'. Tesco's report: '... magnificent Mâcon, showing off Chardonnay's fruitier side'. Oddly enough, I didn't like it much. One more. Waitrose's Good Ordinary Claret 2015, which I awarded a top score in the 2018 edition of Best Wines in the Supermarkets with the description 'This is more than good, it's great' was summarised by a Middlesex online customer of Waitrose with similar conviction. His one word: 'Terrible'.

I suppose I must end this introduction with a word about Brexit. During the currency of this edition, at the end of March 2019, the United Kingdom is expected to take its leave of the European Union. I will not chance any guesses.

The consequences for wine in Britain are uncertain. We do know there will be a transition period but after that the possibilities include the imposition of UK customs duties on wines. They might be similar to those currently imposed throughout the EU on wines imported from various countries outside the union – which will soon enough include us, of course.

Perhaps the most immediate effect will be on personal imports of wine across the Channel. In 2018 the drinks industry body the Wine and Spirit Trade Association said this: 'When Britain leaves the EU, the current allowance of being able to bring back as much wine as you like from the EU will end. There is no limit to the amount you can bring back now for personal consumption without having to pay UK duty. (Some people mistakenly think the limit is 90 litres – 120 bottles – but that is simply the amount above which a customs officer can ask if the wine is for your own use.) It seems unlikely that the Chancellor will condone any 'uprating' of the current allowance for bringing (still only, no sparkling) wine into the UK from outside the EU from just 4 litres'.

UK supermarkets will surely welcome this change. Other consequences of Brexit may be less palatable either to the retailers or to their customers. We must all wait and see, and enjoy a glass of wine while doing so.

Where does the best wine come from?

It's France, I suppose. Fabled estates in Bordeaux, Burgundy and Champagne have a perpetual monopoly on the most-venerated red, white and sparkling wines, worldwide. If your budget per bottle starts at £100 I guess that's all you need to know. But for those of us who buy wine in supermarkets and consider even £10 a bit of a punt, the question needs to be readdressed.

In the global context, you could argue that the country of origin of any wine is immaterial. But the supermarkets wouldn't agree with you. They arrange all the wines in their stores and on their websites precisely according to their nationality.

It's quite odd. You wouldn't display your canned fruits and vegetables this way, would you? Or your frozen fish? Or anything else, really? But that's the way they do the wine and, accordingly, that's the way I arrange the listings in this book.

To be fair, the wines of particular nations and regions do have identifiable attributes even when made from a common grape variety. The white wines from fashionable Sauvignon Blanc, for example, have distinct styles at home in France's Loire Valley and away in the Marlborough region of New Zealand. Chilean Sauvignon has its own qualities, and so does South African.

Germany, though never in fashion, makes inimitably delicious wines from the Riesling grape. Australian wines from this noble variety are so different that I suspect uninitiated devotees of the Mosel and Rhine would hardly recognise a Clare Valley Riesling at all.

While the grape does much to determine the nature of the wine, location still counts for a lot. Landscape and soil conditions, weather and the peculiar skills and customs of the winemakers all have their parts to play.

The French have a word for it: *terroir*, which loosely translates as 'soil', but *vignerons* in France take it to mean the entirety of conditions local to the site of crop production. That's not just the soil but the lie of the land, its geographical position, its climate and indeed what the tillers of that soil and the custodians of the crops get up to.

On visits to France, I have heard much of terroir. Amid the most-valued vineyards of Chablis I have learned that the ground is composed largely of oyster shells, mountainised over millennia into vertiginous slopes. From these bleak, frost-ravaged heights come some of the world's most minerally luscious dry white wines. I've had it all endlessly explained to me and never really understood, but be in no doubt: *grand cru* Chablis is like no other wine.

And so on across all of France. Elsewhere, winemakers might not speak of terroir, but they all believe in the real or imagined unique properties of their estates. They all consider their wines to be an expression of their locations and traditions. This is what gives wine its much-treasured diversity, and of course its mystique. Wine is more than a mere nutritious drug. It's part natural phenomenon, part art form. Hurrah to that, I say.

It's all about the grape variety

The grape, naturally, counts for everything in wine. The finished product is, after all, simply the fermented juice of the fruit. Well, yes, there will be a cultured yeast introduced to assist the process. And there are permitted additives, mostly sulphur products and clarifying agents, to ensure healthy, bright wine. The wine's natural sugars and acids can be supplemented.

But the grape variety still sets the pace. Dark-skinned grapes make red wine because the skins are included in the must (pressed juice) during fermentation and give the wine its colour. The juice of virtually all grapes is clear. You can make white wine with dark-skinned grapes by extracting the juice promptly and fermenting it free of the skins. The base wine for Champagne is made largely from dark-skinned grapes. But still white wine is made much more simply – from pale-skinned grapes fermented without their skins.

Different grape varieties produce correspondingly different wines. There are hundreds of distinct varieties, but a couple of dozen account for most production. All of us have favourites, or at least preferences. The varieties described here account for most of the wines on offer in the supermarkets.

Red wine varieties

Aglianico: Ancient variety of southern Italy said to have been imported by immigrant Greek farmers around

500 BC. The name is a recent rendering of former Ellenico ('Hellenic') and the grape has caught on again thanks to Aglianico del Vulture, a volcanic DOC of Basilicata. The wines are dark, intense, pungent and long-lived.

Barbera: The most widely planted dark-skinned grape of Piedmont in northwest Italy makes easy-drinking purple vigorous rasping red wine to enjoy young and also, increasingly, a darker, denser but still vigorous style given gravitas through oak-ageing. Mostly sold under denominations Barbera d'Asti and Barbera d'Alba. Unrelated to Barbaresco, a Piedmontese wine made from Nebbiolo grapes.

Cabernet Sauvignon: Originally of Bordeaux and the mainstay of claret, Cabernet berries are compact and thick-skinned, making wine of intense flavour and gripping tannin. The grandest wines need decades to develop their full bloom. Everyday wines made worldwide typically have dense colour, purple in youth, aromas of blackcurrants and cedar wood ('cigar box') and firm, juicy-savoury fruit.

Gamay: It's the grape of Beaujolais. Colour can be purple with a blue note; nose evokes new-squashed raspberries with perhaps a pear drop or two, the effect of carbonic maceration, the Beaujolais method of vinification. Fruit flavours are juicy, bouncing, even refreshing.

Grenache: The French name for the Garnacha, originally of Spain, where it is much employed in Rioja and other classic regions. HQ in France is the southern Rhône Valley with further widespread plantings across the country's Mediterranean regions. Wines can be light in colour but emphatic in flavour with a wild, hedgerow-fruit style lifted with spice and pepper. Widely cultivated across the New World.

Malbec: The signature grape of Argentina. A native of Bordeaux, where it plays a minor blending role, it thrives in the high-altitude vineyards of Mendoza, a province of the Andean foothills. The best wines have dark colour and a perfume sometimes fancifully said to evoke leather and liquorice; flavours embrace briary black fruits with suggestions of bitter chocolate, plum and spice.

Merlot: Bordeaux variety very often partnering Cabernet Sauvignon in claret blends and also solo in fabled Pomerol wines including Château Petrus. The grape is large and thin-skinned compared to Cabernet, making wine of rich ruby colour with scents evoking black cherry and cassis and fruit that can be round and rich. Ordinary wines are soft, mellow and early developing but might lack the firmness of tannin that gives balance.

Pinot Noir: It's the solo grape of red burgundy and one of three varieties in champagne. Everyday Pinot wines typically have a bright, translucent ruby colour and aromas evoking red soft summer fruits and cherries. Flavours correspond. Fine Pinot has elegant weight and shape, mysteriously alluring. New Zealand makes distinctive, delicious, sinewy Pinots; Chile produces robust and earthy Pinots; California's best Pinots compare for quality with fabulously expensive Burgundies.

Sangiovese: The grape of Chianti, so-named after the Latin for 'the blood of Jove', makes pleasingly weighted, attractively coloured wines with plummy perfume, even pruny in older wines, and slinky flavours evoking blackcurrant, raspberry and occasionally nectarine. Good Chianti always has a clear tannic edge, giving the wine its trademark nutskin-dry finish.

Syrah: At home in southern France, the Syrah makes wines that at their best are densely coloured, rich in aromas of sun-baked blackberries, silky in texture and plumply, darkly, spicily flavoured. The grandest pure-Syrah wines, such as Hermitage and Côte Rôtie, are gamey, ripe and rich and very long-lived. Syrah is widely planted across Mediterranean France as a blending grape in wines of the Côtes du Rhône and Languedoc. Under the name Shiraz, Syrah is Australia's most prolific red-wine variety.

Tempranillo: The grape at the heart of Rioja has to work hard. The unique selling point of the region's famous red wines is the long ageing process in oak casks that gives the finished product its creamy, vanilla richness – which can all too easily overwhelm the juiciness and freshness of the wine. The Tempranillo's bold blackcurranty-minty aromas and flavours stand up well to the test, and the grape's thick skin imparts handsome ruby colour that doesn't fade as well as firm tannins that keep the wine in shape even after many years in cask or bottle. Tempranillo is widely planted throughout Spain, and in Portugal, under numerous assumed names.

White wine varieties

Albariño: Rightly revered Iberian variety once better known in its Minho Valley, Portugal, manifestation as Alvarinho, a mainstay of vinho verde wine. Since the 1980s, Albariño from Spain's Galicia region, immediately north of Portugal, has been making aromatic and scintillatingly racy sea-fresh dry white wines from vineyards often planted close to the Atlantic shore. The seaside DO of Rias Baixas, now a major centre for gastro-tourism, is the heart of Albariño country. The variety, characterized by small, thick-skinned berries with many pips, is now also cultivated in California, New Zealand and beyond.

Chardonnay: Universal variety still at its best at home in Burgundy for simple appley fresh dry wines all the way up to lavish new-oak-fermented deluxe appellations such as Meursault and Montrachet making ripe, complex, creamy-nutty and long-developing styles. Imitated in Australia and elsewhere with mixed success.

Chenin Blanc: Loire Valley variety cultivated for dry, sweet and sparkling white wines, some of them among France's finest. Honeyed aromas and zesty acidity equally characterize wines including elegant, mineral AOP Vouvray and opulent, golden late-harvested AOP Coteaux du Layon. In South Africa, Chenin Blanc now makes many fascinating and affordable wines.

Fiano: Revived southern Italian variety makes dry but nuanced wines of good colour with aromas of orchard fruit, almonds and candied apricots and finely balanced fresh flavours. Fleetingly fashionable and worth seeking out.

Glera: Widely planted in the Veneto region of northeast Italy, it's the principal variety in prosecco sparkling wine. The grape itself used to be named prosecco, after the winemaking village of Prosecco near Treviso, but under a 2009 change to the wine-denomination rules, the name can now be applied exclusively to the wine, not the grape. Glera makes a neutral base wine with plenty of acidity. It is a prolific variety, and needs to be. Sales of prosecco in Britain have now surpassed those of champagne.

Palomino Fino: The grape that makes sherry. The vines prosper in the *albariza*, the sandy, sun-bleached soil of Andalucia's Jerez region, providing a pale, bone-dry base wine ideally suited to the sherry process. All proper sherry of every hue is white wine from Palomino Fino. The region's other grape, the Pedro Ximenez, is used as a sweetening agent and to make esoteric sweet wines.

Pinot Grigio: At home in northeast Italy, it makes dry white wines of pale colour and frequently pale flavour too. The mass-market wines' popularity might owe much to their natural low acidity. The better wines are aromatic, fleetingly smoky and satisfyingly weighty in the manner of Pinot Gris made in the French province of Alsace. New Zealand Pinot Gris or Pinot Grigio follows the Alsace style.

Riesling: Native to Germany, it makes unique wines pale in colour with sharp-apple aromas and racy, sleek fruit whether dry or sweet according to labyrinthine local winemaking protocols. Top-quality Rhine and Mosel Rieslings age wonderfully, taking on golden hues and a fascinating 'petrolly' resonance. Antipodean Rieslings have more colour and weight often with a mineral, limey twang.

Sauvignon Blanc: Currently fashionable thanks to New Zealand's inspired adoption of the variety for assertive, peapod-nettle-seagrass styles. Indigenous Sauvignons from France's Loire Valley have rapidly caught up, making searingly fresh wines at all levels from generic Touraine up to high-fallutin' Sancerre. Delicate, elegant Bordeaux Sauvignon is currently on top form too.

Semillon: Along with Sauvignon Blanc, a key component of white Bordeaux, including late-harvested, golden sweet wines such as Sauternes. Even in dry wines, colour ranges up to rich yellow, aromas evoke tropical fruits and honeysuckle, exotic flavours lifted by citrus presence. Top Australian Semillons rank among the world's best.

Viognier: Formerly fashionable but perpetually interesting variety of the Rhône Valley makes white wines of pleasing colour with typical apricot aroma and almondy-orchardy fruit; styles from quite dry to fruitily plump.

More about these varieties and many others in 'A wine vocabulary' starting on page 158.

Brand awareness

Big-brand wines such as Blossom Hill and Hardy do not crowd the pages of this book. I do get to taste them, and leave most of them out. I believe they don't measure up for quality, interest or value.

The best wines in the supermarkets are very often own-brands. Own-brands date back to the 1970s, when interest in wine finally began to take root in Britain. Sainsbury's was first, with its own Claret, about 1975. It was hardly a revolutionary idea. Grand merchants like Berry Bros & Rudd (est 1698) had been doing own-label Bordeaux and much else besides, for ever.

In the supermarket sector, wine was bought on the wholesale market like anything else, from butter to washing powder. Only when interest in wine started to extend beyond the coterie served by the merchants did the mass retailers take any notice. It was thanks, of course, to the new craze for foreign travel, and to the good influence of writers like Elizabeth David, who revealed the joys of Continental-style food and drink. In 1966, Hugh Johnson's brilliant and accessible book *Wine* piqued the public consciousness as never before.

The adoption of supermarket wine was slow enough, but accelerated in the 1980s by the arrival of new, decent wines from Australia. Earlier on, cheap Aussie wines had been overripe, stewed rubbish, but breakthrough technology now enabled fresh, bold reds and whites of a different stripe. Wretched Europlonk brands like Hirondelle retreated before a tide of lush Chardonnay and 'upfront' Shiraz.

The horizon for supermarket wine buyers, always shackled by price constraint, was suddenly widened. In spite of the delivery distances, southern hemisphere producers could match their Old World counterparts for value as well as interest and quality.

In time, the winemakers of Europe fought back. Top estates carried on with 'fine wine' production, but humbler enterprises had to learn how to master real quality at the everyday level. They did. I believe the huge improvements in the simpler wines of the Continent owe much to the need to match the competition from the New World.

By the 1990s, Britain had become the world's biggest wine importer. Supermarkets were largely responsible, and now had muscle in the market. They started to dispatch their own people to vineyards and wineries worldwide, not just to buy the wines but to participate in their production. And always, they demanded the lowest-possible prices.

And so to today's proliferation of supermarket own-brands. They are the flagships of every one of the big grocers, and usually the focal point of promotions. They are, naturally enough, the wines of which their begetters are most proud. Mass-market brands do still persist in the supermarkets. Some are very good. I think of Blason, Chasse and Vieille Ferme from France; Baron de Ley and Miguel Torres from Spain; McGuigan and Penfolds from Australia; Catena from Argentina and Concha y Toro from Chile, among others.

If you have a favourite popular brand, do check the index to this book on page 189. It might not be mentioned in the entry for the supermarket where you're used to finding it, but that doesn't mean I've left it out.

My pick of the year

It has been a pleasure to find I have top-scored 30 wines this year. France is the runaway winner with 16 of the wines, followed by Italy with 7, Australia 2 and the rest also-rans. Sainsbury's scoops top retailer with 7 top-score wines with Morrisons and Waitrose next at 5 apiece, 4 for Tesco, 3 each for Aldi and the Co-op, and then the rest.

A reliable guide to the comparative allure of these supermarkets' wine offerings? No way.

Red wines

Wine	Retailer	Price
Morrisons Beaujolais 2017	Morrisons	£5.00
Tesco French Malbec 2017	Tesco	£5.00
Taste the Difference Languedoc Rouge 2017	Sainsbury's	£7.00
Morrisons Nerello Mascalese 2016	Morrisons	£7.50
Solato Lambrusco	Asda	£7.50
Taste the Difference Pic St Loup 2016	Sainsbury's	£8.00
Villa Nardelli Cuvee Carolina 2016	Co-op	£8.99
Le Verdier Cairanne 2016	Morrisons	£10.00
Taste the Difference Barossa Cabernet Merlot 2016	Sainsbury's	£10.00
The Best Toscana 2015	Morrisons	£10.00
Wirra Wirra Cabernet Sauvignon Shiraz Merlot 2015	Co-op	£10.49
Paolo Leo Primitivo di Manduria 2016	Waitrose	£10.99
Finest Viña del Cura Rioja Gran Reserva 2011	Tesco	£11.00
Louis Jadot Beaujolais Quincié 2017	Waitrose	£12.99
Mischief and Mayhem Bourgogne Pinot Noir 2015	Waitrose	£14.99
Terre da Vino Barolo 2014	Waitrose	£18.99

White wines

Wine	Retailer	Price
Exquisite Collection Touraine Sauvignon Blanc 2017	Aldi	£5.49
Finest Saint Mont 2016	Tesco	£6.00
Lot Series Ashwood Estate Pinot Gris 2017	Aldi	£6.99
Vanita Grillo 2017	Co-op	£6.99
Dr L Riesling 2017	Sainsbury's	£7.00
Taste the Difference Languedoc Blanc 2017	Sainsbury's	£7.00
Langhorne Creek Chardonnay 2017	M&S	£9.00
The Best Gran Montaña Reserve Chardonnay 2016	Morrisons	£9.00
Château de Montfort Vouvray 2017	Waitrose	£11.99
Gewürztraminer Steinklotz Grand Cru JP Muller 2012	Lidl	£11.99
Taste the Difference Pouilly Fumé 2017	Sainsbury's	£13.00
Finest Premier Cru Chablis 2016	Tesco	£14.00

Sparkling wines

Wine	Retailer	Price
Exquisite Collection Crémant du Jura 2015	Aldi	£7.99
Sainsbury's Blanc de Noirs Champagne Brut	Sainsbury's	£18.00

Aldi

Aldi is the lowest priced supermarket in the UK. So says *The Grocer* magazine, and it should know, I suppose. Does Aldi have the lowest priced wines? Yes, says *The Best Wines in the Supermarkets 2019*. I have included a dozen good wines from Aldi this year, all European, priced under £5.

Britain's fastest-growing chain (Aldi UK has doubled in size since 2010 and will surpass 1,000 stores in 2020) might also have the fastest-improving wine range overall. Since the German intruder first made it into this guide, a short time ago in the 2013 edition, it has progressed steadily. Aldi's wine offering is already legitimately comparable with most of its rivals.

This year I have picked out several sensationally good Sauvignon Blanc wines from France and given top marks to a Sauvignon Gris from New Zealand. Here too is the cheapest drinkable wine of the year, a Spanish red called Toro Loco ('mad bull') at £3.89. In the context of the sterling:euro rate and the UK tax take, the price seems crazy indeed.

I should add that there's a Toro Loco rosé at the same £3.89. I've scored it as high as any rosé in the book. Readers might infer that I believe this is all you need to spend on rosé. On a quality-value basis, there might well be something in it.

As far as I know, all the wines at Aldi are exclusive. The main own-label brand is the Exquisite Collection range and there is a much-diminished premium range called The Lot series. Most of the wines are available, I am assured, in most of the stores. And all of the wines are on offer online for home delivery.

RED WINES

ARGENTINA

8 Exquisite Collection Argentinian Malbec 2017 £5.99

Argentina has made the Malbec, originally of Bordeaux, its flagship black grape and this one sails worthily under the colours: darkly pungent and peppery black-fruit flavours and a firm grip of tannin all present and correct; 13% alcohol.

8 Don Tomas Terroir Selection Malbec 2017 £7.99

Attractive package delivers smoothly oaked in-character meaty dark Malbec flavours in wholesome balance; 14% alcohol.

9 Finca La Pampa Cabernet Sauvignon 2016 £9.99

Immediately impressive oaked Cabernet in what I might dare to call the modern Bordeaux manner with lush cassis fruit, silky flow and discreet grip; a very safe bet at a justifiable price; 13.5% alcohol.

AUSTRALIA

8 Exquisite Collection South Australian Shiraz 2017 £5.79

Impactful spicy dark mouthfiller which should stand up to the most robustly charred offerings from the barbie; 14% alcohol.

8 Berton Vineyards Durif 2017 £7.49

This deep purple blackberry-blueberry red-meat match from esoteric grape Durif has punch and juiciness; distinctive and satisfying; 14% alcohol.

CHILE

8 Malbec 2017 37.5cl £2.99

Handy half-bottle delivering a roasty-ripe black-fruit savour in the proper Andean Malbec style; 13% alcohol.

RED WINES

CHILE

8 Pinot Noir 2017 £4.79

Textbook bargain Chilean Pinot; light in colour but with plump red fruit and easy charm; 13% alcohol. An equally good match with roast chicken or fish pie.

FRANCE

9 Vignobles Roussellet Pinot Noir £4.49

A Languedoc non-vintage, really quite substantial in its authentic Pinot raspberry-cherry fruit, fortified with a measure of Merlot to add heft and piquant chocolate; an artful contrivance at a giveaway price; 12.5% alcohol.

8 Med Red 2017 £4.49

Generic Midi Grenache-Carignan-Syrah makes an easy-drinking, healthy, ripe and juicy party red; 13% alcohol.

8 Domaine Ferrandière Rouge Reserve 2017 £4.99

Well-made Languedoc, mainly Merlot, has mellow but firmly-edged black fruit and nice weight; 13% alcohol.

9 Domaine Ferrandière Merlot 2017 £5.99

The black-cherry ripeness and mellow chocolate warmth of this trademark Languedoc Merlot are neatly tied off with gentle tannins; artful and friendly; 13.5% alcohol.

ITALY

8 The Fire Tree Sicilian Nero d'Avola Appassimento 2017 £4.99

Soft, intense, near-raisiny speciality red from Sicily is innocent fun; 14.5% alcohol.

9 The Fire Tree Sicilian Riserva 2013 £7.99

Mature oak-aged darkly savoury grilled-meat matcher; has Sicily's warm spice signature and a sleek fruitiness; 14% alcohol.

RED WINES

ITALY

8 **Grande Alberone Zinfandel 2016** **£7.99**

Fancy-looking package which is, I believe, from the Primitivo grape – known as Zinfandel in California. A big, cushiony red, plump with sweet spice and finishing healthily dry; 15% alcohol. Maybe suit pungent cheeses.

NEW ZEALAND

9 **Exquisite Collection New Zealand Pinot Noir 2016** **£6.99**

Bright pigeon's-eye hue and keen strawberry perfume correctly indicate the defined, bright Pinot fruit in this crunchily delicious Marlborough refresher – Kiwi Pinot all the way and well priced; 13% alcohol.

8 **Lot Series Te Haupapa Central Otago Pinot Noir 2017** **£8.99**

Smooth (oaked, I guess) raspberry-plush Pinot of elegant weight and silkiness; 13% alcohol.

PORTUGAL

8 **Animus Douro 2016** **£4.99**

As you'd expect from the Port vineyards, a dark and spicy ripe full(ish) red with a decent grip; 13% alcohol.

ROMANIA

7 **Pinot Noir 2017 37.5cl** **£2.99**

Pale colour just north of rosé and a Beaujolais-like aroma to this cherry-ripe but decently balanced handy half; 12.5% alcohol.

RED WINES

SPAIN

8 **Toro Loco Superior 2016** £3.89
The Aldi house red blends Tempranillo and Bobal to make a lightly coloured but pleasantly briary and grippy throwing wine; 12.5% alcohol.

8 **Toro Loco Bobal Merlot 2016** £4.99
This maroon-coloured Utiel-Requena middleweight red has easy black-cherry fruit with a chocolate suggestion and tidy finish; 13% alcohol.

7 **The Big Gun Spanish Red** £5.49
Non-vintage La Mancha Tempranillo might catch your eye, but it's a bit tough; might suit a fiery curry; 14% alcohol.

PINK WINES

FRANCE

8 **Terres de Brumes Rosé 2017** £4.99
A fleeting grapefruit twang lifts this party-frock pink Mediterranean dry wine; 12% alcohol.

8 **Exquisite Collection Touraine Rosé 2017** £5.99
Perky Loire dry pink, made largely from the Beaujolais grape Gamay. Suitably juicy and fun; 12% alcohol.

8 **Fleur de Prairie Côtes de Provence 2017** £7.49
Discreet onion-skin colour and tangy raspberry perfume to this delicate but well-defined seaside dry pink in a fancy bottle; 13% alcohol. Also in a downsized 18.7cl fancy bottle at £1.99.

SPAIN

7 **Toro Loco Rosé 2017** £3.89
Shell-pink, flowery-smelling but decently brisk strawberry style from Utiel-Requena; alluringly cheap; 12% alcohol.

WHITE WINES

AUSTRALIA

8 **Exquisite Collection Limestone Coast Chardonnay 2017** **£5.79**

Safe unoaked but creamy-appley style from South Australia's pleasingly named cool zone; 13% alcohol.

8 **Exquisite Collection Clare Valley Riesling 2017** **£6.99**

Big flavours here in the true Aussie Riesling style of ripe-apple heft and lingering limey twang; classy dry aperitif and a match for white meat or spicy food; 12.5% alcohol.

CHILE

8 **Exquisite Collection Leyda Sauvignon Blanc 2017** **£5.49**

One of an expanded range of Sauvignons here, with benchmark Chilean ripeness and freshness; 13% alcohol.

FRANCE

9 **Vignobles Roussellet Sauvignon Blanc** **£4.49**

Non-vintage and very cheap generic Sauvignon probably from the Midi (it includes some Colombard) impresses with tangy, sherbetty-gooseberry zest and a grassy lift; artful; 11.5% alcohol.

10 **Exquisite Collection Touraine Sauvignon Blanc 2017** **£5.49**

Eagerly citrussy and grassy textbook river-fresh Loire Valley Sauvignon at a very keen price; a true bargain from Aldi; 12.5% alcohol.

9 **Exquisite Collection Marsanne 2017** **£5.99**

Sunny colour and sweet-blossom nose lead into lush Languedoc ripe white fruits with a lift of citrus and crisp freshness; generous dry white to match white meats as well as creamy dishes and fish; 13% alcohol.

WHITE WINES

FRANCE

8 **Exquisite Collection Picpoul de Pinet 2017** **£6.29**

Sunny ripeness and tangy top notes in this proper Picpoul from Mediterranean France; 12.5% alcohol.

HUNGARY

8 **Lebeges Grüner Veltliner 2017** **£4.99**

Softly-spicy and clean-tasting dry wine in the Austrian Grüner style to match Asian dishes or as an interesting party wine; 12% alcohol.

ITALY

8 **Pianeta Organic Pinot Grigio Delle Venezie 2017** **£5.99**

Eye-catching pot-shaped bottle and organic cultivation add to the standout merits of this plump but mineral and smoky-spicy PG, more in the Alsacien style than the Venetian; nice aperitif with olives; 12% alcohol.

7 **Gavi di Gavi 2017** **£6.99**

Decent effort; Gavi followers should not be disappointed; 12% alcohol.

N ZEALAND

8 **Freeman's Bay Sauvignon Blanc 2017** **£5.99**

Well-priced simple gooseberry-ripe Marlborough wine with brightness as well as slyly seductive sweetness; 12% alcohol.

WHITE WINES

NEW ZEALAND

10 Lot Series Ashwood Estate Pinot Gris 2017 £6.99

This lovely big smoky exotic dry wine from Gisborne has minerality and a citrus twang in ideal counterpoint to its fruit-salad complexity; a conversation-piece aperitif and equally a match for spicy dishes; 13.5% alcohol. Underpriced.

9 Exquisite Collection Marlborough Sauvignon Blanc 2017 £7.49

A better bet than the Freeman's Bay Sauvignon (above) even at the price difference, this has a nice briny attack and long, ripe flavours; 13% alcohol.

PORTUGAL

8 Animus Vinho Verde 2017 £4.99

Friendly elderflower-citrus perfume betokens an agreeably mouthfilling and bright white-fruit off-dry spin on the popular 'green wine' theme of the Minho Valley; 11% alcohol.

ROMANIA

7 Pinot Grigio 2017 37.5cl £2.99

Handy half-bottle of respectable, recognisable PG with an orchardy off-dry freshness; 12% alcohol.

S AFRICA

8 Leaf Plucker Sauvignon Blanc 2017 £6.99

Don't be deterred by the odd name of this mellow Cape variation on the now-ubiquitous Sauvignon theme; plump gooseberry fruit balance with lemony zest; 13% alcohol.

WHITE WINES

SPAIN

8 Toro Loco Blanco 2017 **£4.49**

Distinctive Viura (grape of white Rioja) gives creamy lushness to this bright and fresh Utiel-Requena bargain; 12% alcohol.

8 Exquisite Collection Rias Baixas Albariño 2017 **£6.29**

Convincing grassy rendering of the in-fashion Galician seaside racy dry white; 13% alcohol.

8 The Wine Foundry Godello 2017 **£6.49**

Wordy label proclaims 'Lemons, honeysuckle blossom … lipsmacking zing-zester' and who am I to demur? Likeable Galician fresh dry tapas wine with a crafty residual sweetness and 12.5% alcohol.

SPARKLING WINES

FRANCE

10 Exquisite Collection Crémant du Jura 2015 **£7.99**

Utterly consistent single-vintage pure Chardonnay sparkler from ravishingly lush Jura mountain region east of Burgundy; rush of creamy-apple fruit in the vigorous mousse, crisp and very dry style; 13% alcohol. Top quality, top value.

9 Lacheteau Crémant de Loire Blanc de Noir **£7.99**

Introduced last year, it's eagerly foaming and orchard-fruit fresh with redcurrant juiciness, very dry; made white in the Loire Valley from fast-pressed Cabernet Franc grapes more usually employed for the bright red wines of Chinon and Saumur; 12% alcohol. Pips Prosecco every time.

SPARKLING WINES

FRANCE

8 **Veuve Monsigny Champagne Brut** **£10.99**

Aldi's house champagne is wholesome and balanced, and impressively cheap at the standard shelf price; 12% alcohol.

ITALY

8 **Organic Prosecco 2017** **£7.99**

Untypical Prosecco I call this, not because it's single-vintage or organic but because it has some ripeness of fruit and frisson of flavour within its 'extra dry' style; unusual olde-worlde bottle, too; 11.5% alcohol.

Asda

Will Asda survive the takeover by rival Sainsbury's announced to a shocked nation in 2018? There have been dire warnings from some interested parties, but an Asda spokesperson was reassuring: 'Asda and Sainsbury's will continue to operate as two separate retailers and this proposed merger offers a great deal for customers. There are no planned store closures'.

Sadly, Asda's dedicated online service, the Wine Shop, has already closed. It was a good website that even I was able to operate, making accessible the many wines listed by Asda but absent from any store in my region. You can still order wine as just another grocery item from Asda's overall site for home delivery or 'click and collect' but I suspect availability is not universal, as it was with the Wine Shop service.

Asda's admirable own-label wines make up most of the entries here under their headings Extra Special and Wine Atlas, the very attractively labelled regional series. Highlights this year include an inspired selection of Italian reds including my favourite real Lambrusco, and some good white wines from Spain.

RED WINES

AUSTRALIA

8 **Busby Langhorne Creek Shiraz 2017** **£4.98**

Surprise colour, bright and close to magenta, corresponds with the perky brambly fruit in this friendly red with 14.5% alcohol. Asda suggests a novel food match: barbecued kangaroo.

8 **Extra Special Yarra Valley Pinot Noir 2017** **£7.98**

Good heft and vivid sweet fruit in this typically ripe Aussie Pinot nicely balanced up with a crisp edge; 13% alcohol.

CHILE

8 **Extra Special Carmenère 2016** **£6.00**

Dense crimson – even carmine – colour is matched by concentrated black-fruit ripeness; 13.5% alcohol. Carmenère does have its own special roasty savour – do try one.

FRANCE

8 **Costières de Nîmes 2016** **£5.50**

Excellent purple blueberry and red fruit Mediterranean middleweight dry wine. Characteristic peppery spice and tight dry finish; 14% alcohol. Good with cold pies and meats.

9 **Wine Atlas Ventoux 2016** **£6.18**

Ventoux is a notoriously tough mountain stage on the Tour de France, artfully depicted on the label of this wine from Asda's own-brand Wine Atlas range. Ventoux is also a famous high point among the recumbent vastnesses of the southern Rhône. This is very decent Ventoux indeed, dark, vivid, spicy and gripping; 14% alcohol.

RED WINES

FRANCE

8 Plan de Dieu 2017 **£8.98**

Plan de Dieu is a sought-after village appellation of the Côtes du Rhône where the vineyards occupy a flat zone ('God's plain') of former scrubland where wild herbs such as bay, rosemary and thyme once burgeoned. If you sense ghosts of these familiar aromas in the wine, it might not just be your imagination. A fine full spicy and aromatic red wine; 14% alcohol.

ITALY

8 Extra Special Primitivo 2016 **£5.98**

This warmly spicy Puglian mixed-grill red has firm black fruits and a notion of nutty creaminess from some oak contact; 13.5% alcohol.

9 Extra Special Montepulciano d'Abruzzo 2016 **£6.18**

Juicy and brambly in the proper way of this fun Adriatic wine style, this one also has heft and completeness. Impressive at this price; 13% alcohol. Asda advises that it's brilliantly tasty with casseroles and tomato-based pasta dishes.

10 Solato Lambrusco **£7.50**

Really deep purple colour, cassis and violet nose and sweet but abradingly dry-edged fruit conveyed in a gently fizzing froth of flavours; authentic Lambrusco at a good price to drink thoroughly chilled on any sunny occasion; 11% alcohol.

9 Extra Special Morellino di Scansano 2017 **£7.78**

An all-Sangiovese wine from Tuscany but quite distinct from Chianti, this has its own herbaceous-spicy cherry-blackberry savour and intensity of flavour; 13.5% alcohol. A welcome discovery.

RED WINES

ITALY

8 Extra Special Valpolicella Ripasso 2014 £9.38
A speciality Verona wine made with added concentrated grape must which does have the intended extra density and heft (ordinary Valpolicella is mostly weedy stuff) and you get a satisfying ripe (not raisiny) mouthful of redcurrant and bramble fruit; 14% alcohol.

9 Orbitali Brunello di Montalcino 2011 £18.98
A convincing generic wine from one of Italy's grandest appellations, this is sumptuously dense and ripe with blackberry and thick-skinned plum fruits; sleek and still firmly grippy even at this age. A genuine rendering of the style at a price way below those for single-estate counterparts; 14% alcohol.

NEW ZEALAND

8 Extra Special Marlborough Pinot Noir 2016 £8.50
I liked the green, almost stalky, pungency to the ripe raspberry fruit in this lightly coloured and finely balanced wine; sleek but crisp it will chill well and suit white meat and poultry; 13.5% alcohol.

PORTUGAL

9 Extra Special Douro 2016 £6.00
Red table wine from Port country, made with Port grapes and with a promising Porty nose and the sort of gripping dark spicy-pruny flavours of the fortified wine, without the glycerine, sweetness and viscosity; 13.5% alcohol. Still a satisfying and distinctive beefy red though, and good value at this price.

RED WINES

SOUTH AFRICA

8 **Wine Atlas Cinsault 2017** £5.48

Forward fruit in this vivid Cape varietal is spicy and briary, a good foil for assertively flavoured foods; 14.5% alcohol.

8 **Coffee Pinotage 2017** £8.48

There's a sly richness in the minty-tarry fruit of this eccentrically named Western Cape wine; Pinotage is an acquired taste, and this nicely balanced example makes a trustworthy introduction to the style; 14% alcohol.

SPAIN

8 **Espartero Gran Selection 2017** £5.00

Brisk easy hedgerow-fruit La Mancha Tempranillo with ripeness and even a lick of creamy oakiness; 13.5% alcohol.

8 **Extra Special Old Vine Garnacha 2016** £5.18

'Plausible' I have written unkindly in my note. In fairness, it's a genuinely attractive, sweetly ripe and rounded, gently spiced bargain from the Carineña region; 14% alcohol.

8 **Casa Luis Cariñena Gran Reserva 2011** £6.48

Woody but juicy-blackcurranty big old-fashioned stewpot red which just about lives up to its baroque labelling and is memorably cheap. One of several Casa Luis products from the Cariñena region in Asda, all frequently discounted; 13.5% alcohol. 'Good with mushroom dishes', suggests the back label. I liked this same 2011 wine even better last year; needs drinking up.

RED WINES

USA

8 **Ménage à Trois Midnight 2015** **£9.98**

The name's a mystery but this Californian Bordeaux blend is easy enough to appreciate. It's a cushiony kind of claret (more St Emilion than Médoc if that doesn't sound too facetious), sweetly ripe and rounded but not overcooked and in a good poised balance; 13.5% alcohol.

PINK WINES

FRANCE

8 **Les Estivales Rosé 2017** **£6.98**

Shell pink dry style from the Côtes de Thau with perky raspberry-strawberry scent and bright fruits; 12% alcohol.

WHITE WINES

ARGENTINA

8 **Wine Atlas Torrontes 2017** **£4.98**

The attractive package gives a good platform to Argentina's signature white grape Torrontes. Sweet muscat-grape nose, fruit grapy but artfully dry and delicate, citrus trim; 12.5% alcohol.

AUSTRALIA

8 **Busby Estate Sauvignon Blanc Semillon 2017** **£4.98**

And I thought the sub-£5 Aussie wine had been extinguished by fiscal forces aeons ago. This really isn't bad, teaming tang and tropical flavours for freshness and balance; 11.5% alcohol.

8 **Extra Special Barossa Chardonnay 2017** **£5.98**

'Tree fruit aromas and creamy cashew nut flavours' says Asda of this rather elegant part-oak-fermented and naturally fresh-tasting dry wine; 13.5% alcohol.

WHITE WINES

CHILE

8 **Extra Special Chilean Sauvignon Blanc 2017** **£5.98**

Lively crisp and grassy with the generous ripeness that characterises Chilean Sauvignon; 12.5% alcohol.

FRANCE

8 **Extra Special Bordeaux Blanc 2016** **£6.98**

I suspect the 2017 vintage will be along any minute, but this is the one they offered at the tasting and it was still aboundingly fresh and keen with ripe even tropical fruit notes and that poised acidity that is the hallmark of Bordeaux Sauvignon; 12% alcohol.

8 **Extra Special Chablis 2016** **£11.98**

If your choice is Chablis this is a perfectly good one, flinty, crisp and recognisable; 12.5% alcohol. The price is high, but not exceptionally so.

8 **Sancerre 2017** **£12.68**

'Safe bet' it says in my note, adding that it's pebbly fresh and typical of this famous Sauvignon Blanc appellation at a fair price; 13% alcohol.

ITALY

8 **Extra Special Soave Superiore Classico 2017** **£6.18**

Cool appley freshness and trademark fleeting white-nut creaminess in this well-balanced citrus edge Verona wine at a good price; 12.5% alcohol.

8 **Ca'Mandato Pinot Grigio 2017** **£7.48**

There is still plenty of PG in spite of what I thought was a fading fad. This one from the best spot, Trentino, has good colour and an alluring flowery-spicy nose with nuanced smoky-apple-pear fruits; 12.5% alcohol.

WHITE WINES

ITALY

8 Lugana 2016 £8.98

Lush but crisp Lake Garda wine with a liveliness veering to the spritzy and lots of white-fruit interest; 13% alcohol.

NEW ZEALAND

8 Extra Special Marlborough Sauvignon Blanc 2017 £6.48

Plenty of gooseberry and seagrass in this substantially fruity refresher made with the addition of tiny quantities of Riesling and Gewürztraminer; 12.5% alcohol. Stands out, and the price is keen too.

8 Tukituki Sauvignon Blanc 2017 £6.98

Lots of Marlborough Sauvignon indicators in this lively wine: asparagus and sweet green pepper aromas, grassy raciness and nettly zest; 12.5% alcohol.

SOUTH AFRICA

9 Extra Special Chenin Blanc 2017 £6.00

Crisply defined tropical fruits and honeyed aromas work in agreeable harmony to make this fresh dry wine an affordable delight; 14% alcohol. Drink as an aperitif, or a fine match for roast chicken.

8 Swartland Chenin Blanc 2017 £8.00

Gold colour, sweet-apple scent, integrated flavours taking in tropical fruits, honey notes and citrus; a dry wine of dimension; 12.5% alcohol.

SPAIN

WHITE WINES

9 Extra Special Rueda 2017 £5.48

Melon-peach ripeness and limey-grapefruit acidity work very well together in this all-Verdejo dry wine from the relatively high lands of Rueda north of Madrid; 13% alcohol. Very good buy at this price.

9 Clara Hills Albariño 2017 £7.18

Particularly ripe white orchard fruits fill out this big-flavoured grassy-lush Rias Baixas wine; good balancing citrus acidity completes the picture; 13% alcohol.

8 Extra Special Marques del Norte Barrel-Fermented Rioja 2016 £7.28

Softly ripe sweet-pear/peach fruit in this pale-coloured modern twist on the creamy oxidised Rioja Blanca style of long ago; 12% alcohol.

FRANCE

SPARKLING WINES

8 Extra Special Champagne Premier Cru £19.00

Fresh and defined flavours reflect the majority Pinot Meunier in this full and persistent wine by Louis Bernard; 12% alcohol.

The Co-operative

The Co-op is downsizing. Well, in one sense it is. The really big stores are proving less profitable so they are gradually closing. On the upside, more small-scale convenience stores will be opening. No doubt this makes sense. But will the wine choice be diminished as a result? My local Co-op in rural Somerset has a very limited selection of wine, but the bigger store in rural Wiltshire only a few miles away has a near-comprehensive offering. It's perplexing.

Through its 2,500 stores and huge wholesale operation supplying not just regional Co-op societies but retailers Costcutter, Kwiksave, Mace and Simply Fresh, the Co-op brings a lot of wines to the market. Many are marvellous, if you can find them. You have to do so in person. There's no online service.

This year's top buys include two maximum scores from Italy, some serious reds from the French regions and the house champagne, Les Pionniers, as steadily delicious as ever although modestly elevated in price. I also much like the new Les Pionniers pink champagne – which compared very favourably in appeal with a *grande marque* rosé tasted on the same occasion at more than twice the price.

Fairtrade wines from the southern hemisphere continue to proliferate and to impress at the Co-op, which is rightly proud to be the leading retailer of these products.

RED WINES

ARGENTINA

9 Co-op Fairtrade Cabernet Sauvignon 2017 £6.49

A dark but brightly new-tasting eager blackcurranty pure Cabernet from terrific La Riojana winery; has a lick of luxury from crafty oaking and a hard-to-resist all-round wholesomeness; 12.5% alcohol. One of the Co-op's longest-serving and best Fairtrade wines.

8 Co-op Fairtrade Merlot 2017 £6.49

La Riojana stablemate to the Cabernet above, this is nicely rounded out in its blackberry-cherry ripeness; 12.5% alcohol.

AUSTRALIA

9 The Unexpected Red 2016 £6.49

Unexpectedly perhaps, this odd blend of Sagrantino, Cab Sauv, Tempranillo and Merlot from Victoria State's distinguished Andrew Peace is still available in the same vintage as last year, with its gimmicky film-noir-poster-style label. And it's tasting every bit as alluring: dense purple hue, black (noir?) fruit slicked with oak contact and a grippy Italian-type finish; 14% alcohol.

8 Running With Bulls Tempranillo 2014 £7.99

Presumably a Pamplona tribute by producer Hill-Smith, it's a juicily ripe, dark-hearted and confidently oaked nod to Spain's national grape, but nothing like its most celebrated domestic manifestation, Rioja. A fine vigorous wine all the same; 13.5% alcohol.

RED WINES

AUSTRALIA

10 Wirra Wirra Cabernet Sauvignon Shiraz Merlot 2015 £10.49

No hesitation in top-marking this new vintage in succession to the miraculously good 2014. Grippingly gorgeous McLaren Vale blend with lush black fruits, velvet texture and smooth spices all in perfect harmony; 14.5% alcohol. Utterly consistent perennial of a quality to get excited about, and at an entirely realistic price.

CHILE

8 Co-op Irresistible Bio Bio Valley Malbec 2016 £6.99

Comfortingly baked black fruit in this oaked red-meat wine with a mallability suggesting the Chilean model, as distinct from the edgier Argentine prototype; 13.5% alcohol.

9 Montes Alpha Syrah 2016 £9.99

This big brand from 'water-saving' vineyards in Colchagua is reportedly exclusive to the Co-op. It's a thoroughly seductive creamy-silky plush pure varietal with ripe spice and long, long fruit finishing very tidily; 14.5% alcohol and a nice reminder that good Chilean can be world class.

FRANCE

9 Delas Ventoux 2015 £6.99

Taut and spicy Rhône, abounding in red fruit and sunny intensity. Ventoux has a savoury style of ripeness all its own, and Delas is one of the most dependable producers – owned, curiously enough, by champagne house Louis Roederer; 14% alcohol. Bargain at this price.

8 Château Vieux Manoir 2016 £6.99

Co-op perennial claret has healthy fruit, still coming round, and reassuring weight; 14% alcohol.

RED WINES

FRANCE

9 Domaine des Ormes Saumur Rouge 2015 £7.49
Great to see this classic but elusive red Loire wine at the Co-op: it's purple in colour but rounding out nicely with bottle age, showing lovely leafy-brambly-stalky juicy but sinewy flavours from the Cabernet Franc grape; a standout food-matching red (charcuterie comes to mind) that chills very well to emphasise the brightness of fruit; 13.5% alcohol.

8 Château Lamothe-Bergeron 2012 £13.99
An Haut-Médoc cru bourgeois no less, this succeeds last year's delectable 2009 vintage and could do with more time, but it's already darkly ripe and savoury with liquorous plumpness, gamey and sappy in its fullness; 12.5% alcohol.

8 Domaine les Grandes Costes Pic St Loup 2014 £14.99
Rather grand estate wine matured in oak is still coming round but showing big, spicy ripeness and plenty of lipsmacking black fruit; 14.5% alcohol. Senior wine from a prestige appellation, at a senior price.

8 Châteauneuf du Pape Les Sinards 2016 £19.99
Purple-looking but paradoxically mellow, it stands out for the toasty-spicy ripeness of its complex flavours; fine, savourable special-occasion red with 14.5% alcohol by hyperactive Châteauneuf dynasty Perrin.

RED WINES

FRANCE

8 Savigny-les-Beaune Jean-Jacques Girard 2015 £22.99

Maybe the Co-op isn't the first place you'd look for fine burgundy, but if your local outlet has this one, you can invest with confidence. It looks pale, even callow, in the glass but blooms with developed cherry-raspberry classic Pinot Noir ripeness and exuberance; crunchy but also silky and sleek; 13% alcohol.

ITALY

10 Villa Nardelli Cuvee Carolina 2016 £8.99

Delicious generic Tuscan red by la-di-dah Chianti estate Castello Vicchiomaggio has distinctly Chianti-style vigorous but oak-silked black fruit with the proper nutskin-dry finish; 13.5% alcohol. Decent Chianti, in name or de facto, is elusive at any price in the supermarkets, making this a true star buy.

8 Villa Boscorotondo Chianti Classico Riserva 2014 £15.99

From the same Castello Vicchiomaggio that makes generic Villa Nardelli (above), a classified Chianti of bright, purply, cherry-ripe vigour and luxury heft; 13.5%. The price helps put its excellent stablemate into useful perspective.

SOUTH AFRICA

8 Arniston Bay Fairtrade Shiraz Merlot £6.89

Big brand meets good cause in this surprise blend, delivering a pleasingly weighted and wholesome blackberry and black cherry style finishing briskly tidy; 12.5% alcohol.

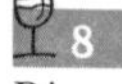

Mount Rozier Merlot 2016 £7.99

Ripe morello cherry sweetness is artfully reined in by the acidity; 14% alcohol; nicely done.

RED WINES

SPAIN

8 **Corte Mayor Rioja Crianza 2014** £8.99

Gaudily labelled brand of Rioja newcomer (well, 1985) Baron de Ley; vanilla-rich but vividly fruity in the best tradition; 13% alcohol.

PINK WINES

FRANCE

8 **Co-op Irresistible Pic St Loup Rosé 2017** £7.49

Pic St Loup is best-known for its muscular reds and this pink spin-off shows plenty of fresh red-fruit flavour; nice pale onion-skin colour and good freshness; 12.5% alcohol.

8 **La Vieille Ferme Rosé 2017** £7.49

Pale shell-pink colour, discreet strawberry-apple aroma and corresponding fresh, crisp but delicately red-fruit sweet flavours make this attractive Rhône brand a safe but pleasing bet; 12.5% alcohol.

8 **La Petite Laurette de Midi Rosé 2017** £7.99

Very pale and brisk dry Mediterranean pink; arrestingly flavoured with red fruits edged with citrus – should make a firm match even for highly flavoured menus; 12.5% alcohol.

WHITE WINES

AUSTRIA

9 **Eitzinger Grüner Veltliner 2016** £8.49

The rightly admired Eitzinger estate in Austria's Kamptal triumphs with this fine lemon-gold-coloured, elegantly weighted, gently abrading brisk spin on the aromatic theme of the indigenous Grüner Veltliner grape; 12.5% alcohol. Smart aperitif, and a nifty match for fish or fowl.

WHITE WINES

CHILE

8 **Co-op Irresistible Leyda Valley Sauvignon Blanc 2017 £7.49**

Typically tropically ripe Chilean style of Sauvignon with a big asparagus whiff, grassy greenness and a proper tang – a winning formula; 13% alcohol.

8 **Indomita Gran Reserva Viognier 2017 £7.99**

Seems a rather martial name for a wine of Bio Bio, close to the Pacific, but this is a friendly full-frontal Viognier, quite dry but plump with apricot fruit and fresh and brisk besides; 13% alcohol.

FRANCE

9 **La Vieille Ferme Blanc 2017 £7.49**

It's not just the chickens on the label, I promise, that make this Mediterranean brand such a perennial favourite. It's a fresh style from a mélange of local grapes evoking peach and pear, mango and white nuts, nicely trimmed with citrus; 13% alcohol. A slick brand of real charm.

9 **Co-op Irresistible Marsanne 2016 £7.99**

This sunny spring-flower-perfumed Pays d'Oc dry white by busy Jean-Claude Mas has a perplexing label design but easy-to-like white and tropical fruit flavours, both lush and refreshing; 13% alcohol.

8 **Co-op Irresistible Chablis 2016 £11.99**

Well-coloured steely style to this elegant pure Chardonnay nicely captures the distinctive Chablis formula. Made by leading local negociant Brocard, it manages to be both bracing and luxuriant; 12.5% alcohol.

WHITE WINES

GERMANY

9 Reichsgraf Von Kesselstatt Riesling Trocken 2015 £10.99

An important change to this Co-op perennial Moselle: previous vintages were QmP wines of the estate's Goldtröpfchen vineyards. This manifestation is a generic Riesling fermented out as a trocken ('dry') wine. All that said, it's a glorious wine, fine gold in colour, racily perfumed with fleeting honey notes and brimming with textbook Riesling zing and depth; 11.5% alcohol.

ITALY

8 Verdicchio dei Castelli di Jesi 2016 £5.99

Don't let the naff amphora bottle and creepy Venus label put you off this artfully balanced white-fruit aromatic just-dry wine lifted by gentle citrus acidity; 12.5% alcohol.

10 Vanita Grillo 2017 £6.99

Sicilian sensation boasts a splendidly overwrought label and delivers a terrifically snappy attack of tangy flavour opening into lush orchard-fruit, mango and grapefruit evocations; 12.5% alcohol. Fine apertif as well as a natural match for shellfish, creamy pastas and risotto.

8 Co-op Irresistible Fiano di Benevento 2016 £6.99

Dry but not austere Campania refresher has a crafty white-nut creaminess to its crisp orchard fruit; intriguing and stimulating; 12.5% alcohol.

9 Co-op Irresistible Gavi 2017 £8.49

Every supermarket seems to have its own Gavi this year, and the Co-op's ahead of the race with this one. It's a particularly minerally and tangy variation on the theme with the proper blanched-almond lick of richness and an emphatic citrus edge; 13.5% alcohol. Nifty match for grilled fish and shellfish.

WHITE WINES

NEW ZEALAND

8 **The Ned Sauvignon Blanc 2017** **£8.99**

Iconic Waihopai River (Marlborough) wine excellently named after local rugged peak seems a little softer than of memory, but still a bright gooseberry-grassy-grapefruit thriller in the best Kiwi tradition with a keen smoky-citrus twang; 13% alcohol. Good partner for smoked fish.

SOUTH AFRICA

9 **Zalze Vineyard Reserve Bush Vine Chenin Blanc 2017** **£8.99**

Particularly crisp and lively Stellenbosch wine with a peachy counterpoint of ripe tropical lushness deep in the flavour; this is a masterful rendering of the ever-fascinating Chenin Blanc variety and further evidence that Cape CBs can be world class; 13.5% alcohol.

SPAIN

7 **Most Wanted Albariño 2017** **£8.49**

Widely available brand from Rias Baixas made by Rioja giant Bodegas Muriel. An easy-drinking grassy refresher without sharp elbows; 13% alcohol.

8 **Cune Rioja 2017** **£8.99**

All white Rioja was once barrel-fermented like this one but today's trend is to keen unoaked flavours of scant distinction. Do try this lemon-brûlée style wine, giving generous expression to the creamy aspirations of the Viura grape while still delivering freshness and tang; 13% alcohol.

SPARKLING WINES

ENGLAND

8 **Balfour 1503 Foxwood Classic Cuvee £16.99**

Well done the Co-op for supporting the now-blossoming English fizzy wine trade; this is a champagne-style (same grapes) sparkler from Kent of delicate charm; 11.5% alcohol.

FRANCE

9 **Champagne Les Pionniers Brut £18.99**

Terrific house champagne made by Piper Heidsieck and in name honouring the Pioneers who set up the Co-operative Movement in the 19th century. Mellow colour, aroma and flavours; outstandingly good and down to 9 points this year only because the price has been hiked in 2018 from £16.99 to £18.99; 12% alcohol.

9 **Co-op Les Pionniers Champagne Rosé Brut £21.99**

New house pink fizz is, like the Co-op's other excellent own-label champagnes, made by Piper Heidsieck, and similarly inspiring. It's a generous smoked salmon colour and it really does taste pink, with strawberry notes alongside the crunchy red fruits, very perky and refreshing but with proper depths of flavour; 12% alcohol. Grand fizz at a grand price, but very fair value: I tasted a Louis Roederer Rosé (£54.99 at the Co-op) alongside and didn't like it more.

SPARKLING WINES

SPAIN

9 **Codorniu Gran Cremant Cava Brut 2015 £9.99**
This alluringly coloured proper sparkler from Catalan giant Codorniu is eager and lemony with apple-pie flavours that stimulate and refresh; 11.5% alcohol. Really well-made and really so much more to it than other fizzes in this price area, may I say.

Lidl

The likeable discounter continues to do regular 'Wine Tours' embracing what can seem rather random selections, usually from France and Spain, rarely from the New World but – curiously – quite often from Hungary. I do try to keep up with the wines featured but have found all too few that would make it into these pages even if they were available year round. Which they are not.

Harrumph. In spite of reassurances I've had from the Lidl team about the core range of wines, I can't say there has been much progress in the last year except for some recent additions from the southern hemisphere, which are claimed to be permanent.

Several of the recommendations I've made in the following rather brief listing are the most recent vintages of wines which have made previous appearances as part of seasonal ranges. Included is a most delectably good and bargain-priced Alsace Grand Cru Gewürztraminer which I hope is becoming an annual event. Lidl's perennial Priorat, Vinya Carles, at £5.99 seriously underpriced, has been coming round for several years and I have high hopes for its continuity.

RED WINES

AUSTRALIA

8 **Winemakers Selection Barossa Valley Shiraz 2017** **£5.99**

Bumper cushiony and wholesome straight Shiraz at a good price; 14.5% alcohol. Boomerangs on the label.

FRANCE

8 **Vinsobres Domaine Crozes-Brunet 2015** **£7.99**

Respectable Rhône village AC scoring a rare 90 (out of 100) by Lidl MW Richard Bampfield and named Top Pick in a 2018 launch. Nicely poised and weighted, dark and spicy, 14% alcohol.

9 **St Emilion Grand Cru 2015** **£10.99**

This hardy Lidl perennial has featured in a persuasive TV commercial and doesn't disappoint. It's already nicely developed, dark and dense in colour and similarly concentrated in its Merlot-dominated black-cherry and cassis fruit; 13.5% alcohol. The price is fair, rather than knock-down.

ITALY

9 **Fortezza dei Colli Chianti Classico 2014** **£5.49**

Still on shelf from last year, a friendly cherry-plump Chianti with trademark nutskin-dry finish to the juicy fruit; 13% alcohol. Still tasting lively and wholesome in 2018, the only change is the price: inexplicaly down from £6.99 to £5.49.

8 **Barolo 2014** **£9.99**

It's certainly the cheapest Barolo on the market, and the best vintage of this one I have tasted so far – limpid coppery-ruby colour, whiff of cherries and roses, easy-weighted silky recognisable Barolo style; 14% alcohol.

RED WINES

SPAIN

8 Baturrica Gran Reserva 2011 £4.99

A brute of a wine from Tarragona region is of considerable age and considerable substance, too. You get the Tempranillo-Cabernet Sauvignon make-up clearly enough in the baked blackcurrant fruit, and a trace of oak softens the sinews of over-ripeness. Main merit? I bought a bottle on promo at £2.99, and it was very drinkable with a fiery Mexican hotpot; 13% alcohol.

9 Priorat Crianza Vinya Carles 2014 £5.99

Not a core-range wine but one to watch out for as it has turned up periodically in successive vintages. Priorat is a cult Catalan site making big, rich reds usually at corresponding prices. At £5.99 this discreetly oaked and silky medium-heft, sweet-violet-centred black-fruit red-meat matcher is a distinctive and distinctly affordable introduction to the style; 14% alcohol.

WHITE WINES

CHILE

8 Cimarosa Pedro Jimenez 2016 £3.99

A mildly exotic melon aroma draws you into this dry and citrus-edged party white with a style of its own; 13% alcohol.

WHITE WINES

FRANCE

Chablis 2015 **£9.99**

Maturing but still lush and perky, this is an authentic wine with proper minty Chablis-Chardonnay minerality in a leesy rather than flinty style; 12.5% alcohol. Price is up from last year's £8.99.

10 **Gewürztraminer Steinklotz Grand Cru JP Muller 2012** **£11.99**

A rare treat from Alsace – gold in colour and with aromas of lychee, ginger, Sauternes-like honey and trademark rose petals; it is almost dry, but gravid with exotic, spiced fruit flavours; unlike sweet everyday Gewürz, this single-vineyard wine is in perfect balance, poised to refresh as well as to intrigue; 13% alcohol. Not a core-range wine but it has cropped up in more than one vintage at Lidl.

SPAIN

8 **Abellio Albariño Rias Baixas 2017** **£6.29**

Now-ubiquitous dry white from Galicia in Spain's Atlantic northwest, this is tangy-fresh with a bit of citrus sharpness at the edge of the grassy fruit; 12.5% alcohol. Nice label.

Majestic

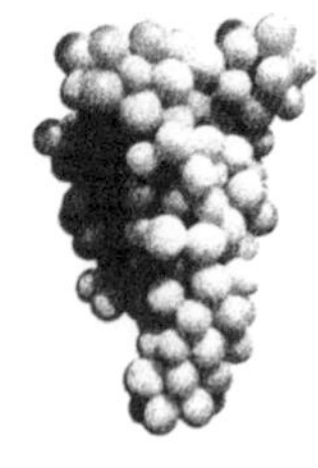

Marvellous tasting of Majestic wines this year was held in a vast new space high above one of the stands at Lord's Cricket Ground in London. Marvellous wines too, but many were samples from small parcels bought in by the clever Majestic team and these would all have been sold out before this book gets to press.

This lengthy tale is a preamble to the brevity of the Majestic entry in this edition. Still plenty of interest here, I hope, and be assured that the quality and diversity of this enterprising retailer are still scoring well.

A word about prices. Now that Majestic has shrugged off the myth of its 'wholesale only' licence, which obliged customers to buy at least 12 bottles – and briefly six bottles – at a time, it has adopted a new method of persuading shoppers to go for quantity. All wines are offered at two prices. One is for the single bottle if your purchase is five or fewer bottles. The other is the 'mix six' price. To qualify, as you might have already guessed, you just need to buy six or more bottles per visit.

The prices I give here are all 'mix six'. They represent a discount of between 10 and 25 per cent on the single-bottle price. The same discounts apply equally in the stores (more than 200 around the country) and online. Home deliveries are made from branches free of charge for orders of six bottles or more. Online orders worth £150 and above are despatched free by courier.

RED WINES

CHILE

8 **Marea Syrah Valle de Leyda 2012** £12.99
Deep opaque colour and vivid blackberry nose lead on to keen defined fruit featuring notes of bitter chocolate and a chilli trace all in an agreeable velvet texture; 14.5% alcohol.

FRANCE

8 **Definition Claret Médoc 2014** £9.99
Good of its kind, so much so that this well-made Bordeaux needs more time to reach what might be its intended peak of maturity, this is reasonably priced and a safe investment for the future; 13% alcohol.

8 **Mas de la Dona Côtes du Roussillon Villages 2017** £9.99
Deep purple young but developed Mediterranean wine combining blueberry-briar juiciness with spicy savour; 15% alcohol.

8 **Les Hauts Vignes Cairanne 2016** £11.99
This silky spicy Côtes du Rhône brims with intense purple-fruit flavours and grippy tannins; finely weighted; 14% alcohol.

ITALY

8 **Cantina di Venosa Terre di Orazio Aglianico del Vulture 2013** £7.99
Who can resist any wine with the word Vulture in its name? This is a maturing dark-hearted red, gamey even truffly in its bitter-chocolate depths, and still with a good grip to match big-flavoured meats including sausages; 14% alcohol.

RED WINES

ITALY

8 **Corolla Nero d'Avola 2016** £7.99
Easy-weighted Sicilian brambly summer red with hints of pepper and island spice; 13% alcohol.

N ZEALAND

8 **Russian Jack Pinot Noir 2014** £11.99
From Martinborough Vineyards (pioneers of Kiwi Pinot) a pale but definitely interesting crunchy red-fruit ripe and sleek wine of pleasing weight; 12.5% alcohol.

SPAIN

8 **Finca Carelio Tempranillo VdT 2015** £7.99
Eye-catching avian label for this wine from 'the wild plains of Northern Castile' reveals a big blackcurranty red of some maturity and good grip; 14% alcohol.

8 **Arc de Pedra 2016** £12.99
Gamey, darkly savoury complex black-fruit middleweight from the much-admired Catalan region; good for the grander kind of barbecue occasion; 14% alcohol.

USA

9 **Horse Heaven Hills Merlot 2015** £14.99
From Washington State in the American northwest, a blood-red, gorgeously dark-hearted Pomerol-style monster without a trace of over-ripeness; very nicely defined fruit; 15% alcohol.

PINK WINES

FRANCE

8 **Commanderie de Peyrassol Rosé 2016** £11.99
Swish Côtes de Provence wine with pale shell-pink colour and alluring lemon-tinged strawberry perfume and fruit, dry and crisp but generous in its delivery; 12.5% alcohol.

WHITE WINES

AUSTRIA

9 **Definition Grüner Veltliner Niederösterreich 2017** **£8.99**

Bloomy aromatic trace-of-muscat perfume to this fresh and crisp but exotically contrived spicy dry wine from Lower Austria; 12.5% alcohol. Good value.

CHILE

8 **Aresti Bellavista Sauvignon Gris 2016** **£7.99**

A kind of smoky variation on Sauvignon Blanc, brightly fresh in spite of relative age and with a limey twang; 12.5% alcohol.

FRANCE

8 **Viognier Paul Jaboulet Ainé 2017** **£8.99**

Rhône wine with the expected apricot aroma of Viognier but not the usual plump sweetness; this is restrained, fresh and crisp; works well; 12.5% alcohol.

8 **Domaine de Vaux St Georges Sauvignon Blanc 2017** **£9.99**

Seductive apple-blossom nose and long green fruit in this Touraine (Loire Valley) wine confer both immediate appeal and lingering flavours; 12.5% alcohol.

8 **St Véran Geoffrey Martin 2016** **£14.99**

A fine rush of eggy-rich sweet-apple Chardonnay in this luxurious Mâconnais dry wine; 13% alcohol. Seafood partner.

ITALY

8 **Araldica Cortese 2017** **£7.99**

Straight grassy and sweet-nut balancing act from Piedmont; aromatic and refreshing; 12% alcohol. If this tastes to you like trendy and pricier Gavi, it's because it's made in the same part of Italy, from the same grape variety.

WHITE WINES

ITALY

8 La Raia Il Borgo Gavi 2016 £10.99

Notably zesty style to this flavoursome chi-chi Piedmont dry white; long slaking vegetal-peachy fruit with a lemon twang; 12.5% alcohol.

PORTUGAL

8 Porta 6 Vinho Verde 2017 £7.99

This really is quite *verde* (green) in the indigenous Minho Valley manner of its origin and there's a correct, just-detectable spritz; bracing and refreshing with the intrusion, sadly, of residual sweetness at the edge; 9.5% alcohol.

SOUTH AFRICA

8 Definition Chenin Blanc 2017 £9.99

Finely balanced peach-pear honey-citrus dry style for aperitif drinking; 14% alcohol.

8 Gabb Family Chardonnay 2017 £9.99

Bright Stellenbosch pure varietal from ripe peachy-melon fruit enriched with time in oak and edged with citrus; comforting and poised; 14% alcohol.

FORTIFIED

SPAIN

9 La Canoa 12-Year-Old Palo Cortado Sherry £12.99

Handsome amber colour, smoky-figgy nose, nutty-rich but almost austerely pure in its pungent rancio flavours, this is an outstanding dry, long-aged sherry at a perfectly sensible price; 20% alcohol. Drink chilled with unadorned nuts or preserved fruits.

Marks & Spencer

Pondering the wine sections in M&S, as I always do when visiting the stores for any reason, I often find the spaces cramped, the choice limited, and the supply of wines under £10 all-but absent.

Knowing as I do just how broad and deep the M&S wine range really is, it's a disappointment. I'm not sure this great retailer is maximizing its opportunities in the wine department.

I have recommended about 60 M&S wines this year, and these are just a modest cross-section of the whole. Prices start at £5.00 – oh yes, there are plenty of 'entry level' wines on offer – and the quality is consistent at every price point. This is just an introduction. To make a leisurely inspection of the wider choice, look at M&S wine online.

All the wines on the website, barring a few very costly individual items, are offered in six-bottle cases. There are always price promotions, including frequent offers of up to 25 per cent off for orders of any two or more cases. You begin to see why M&S seems to be doing better online than it is through its shrinking network on our high streets.

I do hope the downbeat media reporting (including my own footling complaints) of this great enterprise isn't putting anybody off the wines. They've never been better. The New World offerings, from the likes of Chile and Australia, are astoundingly good, and this year there is a brand new house champagne range. Something definitely to celebrate at M&S.

RED WINES

ARGENTINA

9 **Craft 3 Malbec 2017** £10.00

Deeply crimson fruit bomb from Mendoza by former M&S winemaker Gerd Stepp (he still also makes wine in the Rhineland); magnificently mouthfilling and joyfully juicy with blackberry flavours and a perfectly judged crisp finish; 14% alcohol. A standout wine amid the Mendoza Malbec crowd.

8 **The Party Malbec 2017** £14.00

Label's a bit of a muddle, but the wine's spicy-peppery extravagant black fruit intensity is easy enough to appreciate; fine unoaked Mendoza pure varietal for special occasions; 14% alcohol.

CHILE

9 **Chilean Cabernet Sauvignon 2017** £5.00

Arrestingly natural ripe, juicy and balanced Cabernet; hits the spot; 13% alcohol. Top value.

8 **Tierra Y Hombre Pinot Noir 2017** £7.00

In the fuller, riper style of Casablanca Pinot, a brightly red-summer-fruit wine to match poultry or saucy fish dishes; 13.5% alcohol.

ENGLAND

8 **Halfpenny Green Penny Red 2016** £9.50

I must give this enterprising Staffordshire wine my stamp of approval. It's in the style of a country wine, though from grapes, with the most recognisable variety the Pinot Noir (at just 15% of the blend) giving raspberry juiciness to the whole. Likeable lively picnic red; 12% alcohol.

RED WINES

FRANCE

8 Domaine de Brignac 2016 £6.00
Carignan-based Pays d'Hérault delivering juicy hedgerow-cherry fruits with spicy warmth; 11.5% alcohol.

8 La Fleuve Bleu Rouge 2017 £6.00
Yachty label gives a clue to the Mediterranean origin of this firm but friendly red-fruit picnic wine; 12% alcohol.

7 Beaujolais 2017 £9.00
Purple and rather sweetly ripe, I thought, but squishy and fun; 12.5% alcohol. Seems expensive.

8 Château les Rambauds Malbec 2016 £9.50
Unusual Bordeaux red, comprising only Malbec; makes an impression with its roasty darkness and savoury grip; no oak but smoothly textured; 13% alcohol.

9 Plessis-Duval Saumur Champigny 2017 £10.00
Bright maroon colour betokens this suitably vigorous stalky-leafy purple-tasting grippy Cabernet Franc from one of the great red-wine appellations of the Loire; 12.5% alcohol. Drink cool with picnics, cold meats, creamy cheeses.

8 Crozes-Hermitage Cave de Tain 2016 £13.00
Nicely briary and abrading pure Syrah from famed northern Rhône appellation with bright and grippy red fruit; 12.5% alcohol.

9 Bichot Hautes Côtes de Beaune 2015 £14.50
Blissfully good ready-to-drink burgundy, has a sweet raspberry-strawberry perfume and entirely consistent ripe and poised fruit; silky, elegant and long; 12.5% alcohol. A safe investment for roast birds or game.

RED WINES

ISRAEL

8 **Recanati Carignan Petite Sirah 2016** £11.00
Unexpected crimson vanilla-rich spicily fruity austerely dry-finishing hefty developed food wine (lamb tagine, I've written down, mysteriously) from the Judean Hills; 14% alcohol.

ITALY

8 **Reggiano Rosso 2016** £7.00
Old favourite from the usually unpromising plains of Emilia Romagna, a blend of three distinct Lambrusco varieties and does indeed resemble the bright cassis style of the newly repopularised fizzy red. But this one is perfectly still, sweetly ripe but crunchily dry at the finish; 12% alcohol. Drink cool with cold meats, bold cheeses and, if you take M&S's advice, sausage pasta!

8 **Negroamaro Cantine San Marzano 2016** £8.00
Soothing savoury pleasingly charred black fruit in this Puglian red-meat wine has heft and length and a fine corrective finish; 13.5% alcohol.

8 **Teroldego Rotaliano 2016** £9.00
From subalpine Trentino, an indigenous herbaceous plummy/red-fruit food wine (roast pork and birds, cold meats) of likeable distinctiveness; 12.5% alcohol.

NEW ZEALAND

8 **Koha Merlot 2016** £11.00
In aroma and fruit, this Hawke's Bay varietal has a beguiling black-cherry-caramel savour made all the more likeable by the balancing brisk dryness and grip at the finish; 12.5% alcohol.

RED WINES

NEW ZEALAND

9 **Te Taha Martinborough Pinot Noir 2016 £16.00**
Martinborough is the original fountainhead for Kiwi Pinot and this gloriously ripe and clingy wine, made in what I take to be the burgundian style (no oak though), is worthy of the provenance; lovely silky partner for roast duck and other meaty treats; 14.5% alcohol.

SOUTH AFRICA

8 **Zebra View Fairtrade Cabernet Sauvignon 2017 £7.00**
Dense sweetly ripe, almost tarry, but thoroughly wholesome squished-black-fruit upbeat young-at-heart Swartland wine made with the best intentions; 14% alcohol.

SPAIN

9 **Las Falleras Red 2017 £5.00**
Awesomely consistent Valencian party wine with vivid purple-ruby colour, juicy berry ripeness and a healthy completeness rounded off with correcting tannic grip; 12% alcohol.

8 **Marques de Alarcon Tempranillo Syrah 2017 £7.00**
The elaborate label might hint at the Rioja style but this La Mancha red is not that kind of wine at all. An unoaked perky juicy blackcurrant fruit and somehow thoroughly Spanish blend; 13.5% alcohol.

9 **Rioja Perez Burton 2015 £12.00**
It carries no designations of Crianza/Reserva status and unusually names the constituent grape, Tempranillo, on the front label. But this is a serious-quality velvet-oaked maturing silky cassis Rioja of the best kind; 14% alcohol.

Marks & Spencer

PINK WINES

FRANCE

8 **House Rosé 2017** £5.00

Shell pink, sweet-bloom nose, red-fruit freshness, delicately dry; 12% alcohol. Made by excellent Plaimont co-op and a bit of a bargain.

N ZEALAND

8 **Marlborough Rosé 9.5% 2015** £11.00

'Naturally produced lower-alcohol' wine gets a mention here because it tastes perfectly normal: bright dry red-fruit pink with unremarkable heft and yes, 9.5% alcohol.

SPAIN

8 **Raso de la Cruz Rosé 2017** £6.00

Delicate fresh strawberry style finishing neatly dry from Garnacha and Tempranillo; 12.5% alcohol.

8 **Angelito Rosado 2017** £8.50

This Navarra pink has a pale copper hue, bright dry delicately cassis and raspberry fruit, notably refreshing and crisp; 12.5% alcohol.

WHITE WINES

ARGENTINA

8 **El Cuando Chardonnay 2017** £7.00

Apple-pie Mendoza dry wine with a tiny dose of sweetening Torrontes to gave a grapey trace; 12.5% alcohol.

8 **La Posada Fairtrade Pinot Grigio 2017** £9.00

Everybody else is doing PG, so why not Argentina? From La Riojana co-operative in the Fairtrade scheme, a fresh, gently spicy dry style full of white fruit; 12.5% alcohol.

WHITE WINES

AUSTRALIA

9 Australian Chardonnay 2017 £5.00

Basic Aussie Chardonnay has had a deservedly bad press of late. Here's a mould-breaker: keen, mineral, fresh and balanced pure apple-peach Chardonnay fruit in an artful blend with 15% other varieties by De Bortoli; 12.5% alcohol. Safe bet and a bargain.

10 Langhorne Creek Chardonnay 2017 £9.00

Luscious unoaked pure Chardonnay, it's a breath of fresh air: lovely fleshy apple and ripe peach fruit evocations and a whole range of citrus twangs to scintillate and balance; just seems perfect to me and full of life; 12.5% alcohol.

8 Pheasant Gully Semillon Chardonnay 2017 1.5l pouch £13.50

Yes, a marsupial-style Aussie pouch containing a nicely balanced apple/pineapple fresh tangy-finishing party dry white at the equivalent of £6.75 per bottle; 12.5% alcohol. There are other pouches available including non-marsupial varieties but this was the one I liked best.

CHILE

8 Chilean Sauvignon Blanc 2017 £5.00

Nicely balanced party dry white with hallmark Chilean sunny ripeness and good freshness; 12.5% alcohol.

9 Puzzle Tree Chardonnay Viognier 2017 £6.00

A new wine (to me) and it instantly charms with its generous colour, nectarine-tropical aromas, seductive stone-fruit and orchard-fruit combo of lush flavours (some oak contact) and nifty finishing twang; 13% alcohol. Very good buy.

WHITE WINES

CHILE

8 Tierra Y Hombre Sauvignon Blanc 2017 £7.00
Plenty of ripeness lifted by a perky asparagus pungency to the grassy Sauvignon flavours and citrus crispness; 12.5% alcohol.

9 Pintau Viognier 2017 £9.50
New spin on what currently seems to be a bit of a Viognier revival, a limpid yet mineral style to the thematic apricot-nectarine fruit in this lush balancing act from the Colchagua Valley. Distinctive dry wine of a contemplative nature for shellfish, white meats or awkward salad dishes; 13.5% alcohol.

ENGLAND

8 English White Lily 2017 £10.00
In case you're trying to guess what sort of wine a blend of Surrey-grown Ortega, Müller-Thurgau and Bacchus grapes makes, dare I suggest shades of Sauvignon Blanc? Grassy, fresh, rewarding dry white by Denbies; 11.5% alcohol.

8 Denbies Pinot Gris 2016 £16.00
Special-occasion dry exotic wine from the Surrey Downs with traces of sweet apple, honeycomb and woodsmoke – a Pinot Gris neither in the unctuous Alsace style nor the vapid Veneto style either, but in, I guess, the Surrey style, which includes a bit of Chardonnay. Oak-fermented and brought up, it's a legitimate dry-finishing and maybe pioneering still English wine; 12.5% alcohol.

WHITE WINES

FRANCE

8 Le Bois Doré Saumur Blanc 2017 £8.00

This is the driest, greenest manifestation of the Loire's wondrous Chenin Blanc. Very crisp, fresh and lemony; 12.5% alcohol.

8 Domaine Mandeville Viognier 2017 £9.00

It feels like decades since the brief craze for Viognier began and ended, and here's a welcome reminder of what it was about: distinctive apricot nose and fruit made upliftingly fresh and interesting by fine citrus acidity; 13% alcohol.

8 Château Moncontour Vouvray Demi-Sec 2017 £10.00

Not as sweet as the description demi-sec might aver, this Loire Chenin Blanc is a masterclass in balance between richness of peachy-orchard fruits and piquant citrus acidity; 12% alcohol. Fine aperitif and also a match for fruit tarts and noisy cheeses.

8 Picpoul de Pinet 2017 £10.00

Picpoul is everywhere, but invariably interesting. This one has lots of leesy interest to the tangy white orchard fruit; a fine oyster match; 12.5% alcohol.

8 Réserve du Boulas Laudun Côtes du Rhône Villages 2017 £10.00

White CdR can be thrillingly ripe and fascinating. This one qualifies. A fruit salad of tropical, citrus and orchard fruits, lush and aromatic and yet dry and fresh and bright; 14% alcohol.

WHITE WINES

FRANCE

8 **Bourgogne Chardonnay 2015** **£12.00**

The sweet-apple style to this mature wine is expensively leesy and creamy below the perky fruit; the generic burgundy I liked best on the day; 13% alcohol.

GEORGIA

8 **Tbilvino Qvevris 2015** **£10.00**

Splendid orange-gold oxidative traditional Georgian wine from white Rkatsiteli grapes fermented with their skins and matured in clay amphorae buried in the ground; gently pungent, peachy and very dry; 12% alcohol. Let's hear it for diversity.

GERMANY

8 **Darting Dürkheimer Riesling 2017** **£10.50**

This lemony and briskly dry Rheinpfalz aperitif wine is racily stimulating and delicious with shining green-apple fruit and fine balance; 10.5% alcohol.

GREECE

9 **Atlantis Santorini 2017** **£12.00**

It's as if the volcanic soil of the caldera that forms the chi-chi Aegean island resort transfers its spicy salinity into the wine. Silly, of course, but that's wine for you. This is a crackingly refreshing and briny dry food wine (fish, fowl, salads and more); 13% alcohol.

WHITE WINES

ITALY

8 Falanghina Beneventano 2017 **£7.50**

Well-coloured Campania dry wine with herby aromas and rather exotic peach and sweet-melon fruits, all nicely trimmed up in brisk acidity; 12.5% alcohol. Grows on you.

8 Soave Classico 2017 **£8.50**

Bright and tangy rendering of the well-loved Verona wine with the right green-gold colour, lemon-apple-nutty style and freshness all the way; 12.5% alcohol.

9 Alta Luna Gewürztraminer 2017 **£9.50**

The Traminer grape, begetter of the Gewürz of Alsace, supposedly hails from subalpine Italy, so here's an ancestrally interesting rendering. I loved its keen lychee pong, spiced fruits and controlled sweetness; 13.5% alcohol. A better buy than M&S's own oversweet Alsace Gewürz.

8 Pecorino Terre di Chieti 2017 **£11.00**

The fad for putting sheep on the labels of Pecorino wines seems to be being put out to grass. This fine Abruzzo dry nutty white has a nice tree instead. Lots of sapid white-fruit ripeness here on the way to the tangy finish; 12.5% alcohol. Good with fish dishes from prawn cocktail to scallops.

WHITE WINES

NEW ZEALAND

9 **Seifried Estate Grüner Veltliner 2017** **£11.00**

'Lemon meringue pie' I've written in a flailing attempt to summarise the delights of this spiffy confection. It has delicate pear and citrus notes within the discreetly spicy and lively style, dry and distinctive; 12.5% alcohol. Don't seek to compare this with the Austrian model, just enjoy it with fish, savouries and cheeses.

SOUTH AFRICA

9 **Bohoek Semillon 2016** **£10.00**

M&S claimed this was a new vintage, but I tasted this 2016 last year and loved it. Still vivid with pineapple, nectarine and lemon verbena aromas and flavours, a discreetly oaked dry wine with long, lush flavours and 12.5% alcohol.

8 **Villiera Barrel Fermented Chenin Blanc 2017** **£12.00**

Buttered toast comes irresistibly to mind on sniffing this gold-coloured, ambrosia-scented, rich-but-poised extravagantly oaked lobster wine; 14% alcohol. Maybe a shade over the top but what a treat.

9 **Paul Cluver Elgin Riesling 2017** **£13.00**

Limey-bright and racily mineral apple-crisp pure varietal with fine fruity heft and ripeness as well; a remarkable and unexpected style from the Cape; 10.5% alcohol. Aperitif duty or a partner for Asian menus.

WHITE WINES

SPAIN

9 **Las Falleras White 2017** **£5.00**
Soft but clean-tasting Valencian off-dry party white from Viura grapes; 12% alcohol.

FORTIFIED

PORTUGAL

8 **Extra Dry White Port** **£13.00**
Dry rather than extra dry I'd call it, but a good sweetly spirity spin on a rather neglected theme to be drunk icy cold as an aperitif; 20% alcohol. Made by Taylor's of Chip Dry White Port fame.

9 **Ten Year Old Tawny Port** **£15.00**
The coppery colour hints at more than a decade in cask and the lovely sweet figgy-nutty nose likewise; silky and supple fruits with just the right notion of fire in this finely adjusted old wine by Taylors; 20% alcohol. Bought online as part of a Christmas mixed port case, generously reduced in the New Year.

SPARKLING WINES

AUSTRALIA

8 **Craft 3 Sparkling Brut** **£12.00**
From the same grape varieties that go into champagne, a tank-made foaming (as distinct from fizzing) dry sparkler with nuances of champagne flavour; 12% alcohol. Fun and fair value.

SPARKLING WINES

FRANCE

8 **Marquis de Goulaine Crémant de Loire Brut** £15.00

Chenin Blanc gives this fully sparkling wine a rich fruitiness of a very endearing kind, yet it finishes brightly dry and fresh; 12% alcohol.

8 **Champagne Delacourt Brut** £30.00

I never thought this would happen. Oudinot, M&S's house champagne since the dawn of time, has been replaced by an entirely new name, Delacourt. It's a 'richer style' says M&S winemaker Sue Daniels, who worked with 'a predominantly female winemaking team' in Champagne to create the range. Well, I certainly liked this non-vintage launch wine, full of ripe red-apple fruit, bready aromas and mellow conviviality; 12.5% alcohol. Price seems high for house champagne.

8 **Champagne Delacourt Medium Dry** £30.00

Extending the 'richer' theme of the new house champagne this is contrived sweeter wine (four times as much sugar 'dosage' as the brut wine) which I liked quite a lot. If you don't like your champagne too green, try this; 12.5% alcohol.

9 **Champagne Delacourt Blanc de Blancs Brut 2008** £35.00

My pick of the new Delacourt champagnes and only £5 more than the non-vintage wines; rich colour, warm bakery nose, mellow, complex and long; 12.5% alcohol.

Morrisons

Morrisons' wine has long seemed to me understated and just a little indistinct. But following this year's huge tasting, I can feel the fog lifting.

The main attraction is the own-label wine. There are two levels: the 'Signature' series bearing the autograph Wm Morrison [founder 1899] followed by 'Specially selected'. In the following pages I'm prefixing these wines simply as 'Morrisons'. The premium own-label range The Best I have designated, surely with unarguable logic, with the prefix The Best.

Between them, these two ranges have garnered four maximum scores. I think the Morrisons Beaujolais 2017 at £5.00 is exemplary, and The Best Gran Montaña Reserve Chardonnay 2016 at £9.00, made co-operatively by Morrisons and a local winery in Argentina, is an object lesson. Sicily and Tuscany respectively supply the two other 10-pointers; both are quite remarkable.

There are high-scoring wines in particular plenty from France, Italy and Spain. In my local branch, a middlingly large store, I'm glad to report that most of these wines do appear on the shelves – which now seem as sensibly arranged as at any other time.

Any wines you cannot find in your own local store might be available on the messy Morrisons 'Wine Cellar' website. I'm not sure this facility is entirely up to date: the current vintage listed for the formidable Morrisons Beaujolais 2017 when I last looked was 2013.

RED WINES

ARGENTINA

9 **The Best Gran Montaña Reserva Malbec 2016** £12.00

Deep crimson colour and a sun-baked black-fruit nose precede deluxe minty bitter-chocolate matching flavours in this big smoothie created by the Morrisons team with La Agricola winery; 13.5% alcohol. If there is such a thing as an ideal steak wine, this might be it.

AUSTRALIA

8 **The Best Limestone Shiraz 2017** £7.00

Dark and cushiony in appearance and disposition, it has a roasty flavour and intense briar fruit with soft spice and an easy finish; 15% alcohol.

8 **Workshop Wine Company Uncaged Barossa Shiraz 2016** £7.25

This sweetly ripened long and lush monster (15% alcohol) is actually quite restrained. Not tame nor wild neither – a nice domesticated creature I'd say.

CHILE

8 **Head Honcho Pinot Noir 2016** £5.50

Not sure about the cat-in-the-hat label graphic but this is an entirely convincing sunny-ripe Central Valley wine generous with the raspberry and cherry juiciness and nicely plump; brisk, tight, 13.5% alcohol and cheap.

8 **The Best Chilean Pinot Noir 2017** £8.00

Full-of-fruit, silky, typical oaked Chilean Pinot by Cono Sur – mellow and substantial; 14% alcohol.

RED WINES

CHILE

8 **Root 1 Carmenère 2017** **£8.00**

The fine colour might just be the carmine red that reputedly gives the Carmenère grape its name. A big distinctive wine combining briar and cassis fruits with notes of both coffee and toffee all in happy harmony; 13% alcohol.

9 **The Best Single Vineyard Chilean Pinot Noir 2015** **£12.00**

Made by esteemed Errazuriz, a proper premium Pinot with earthy-silky elements to the exuberantly ripe raspberry cherry fruit; 13.5% alcohol. It's not an attempt to ape the burgundy style but is instead the best Chilean style, and that's just fine.

FRANCE

10 **Morrisons Beaujolais 2017** **£5.00**

Eager purple colour and a juicy purple pong positively jump out of the glass to welcome you to this deliciously perky, new-squished, ripe berry-fruit bouncer. It's everything a simple Beaujolais should be, and all at a better-than-bargain price; 13% alcohol.

8 **Les Vallons Bordeaux 2015** **£6.75**

Generic claret, pleasingly grounded in its flavours with wholesome blackcurrant ripeness and natural balance; 13% alcohol.

RED WINES

FRANCE

9 The Best Côtes du Rhône Villages 2016 £7.00

Big flavours and an easy weight mark out this exceptionally enjoyable spicy-grippy mellowing red-fruit wine with 14% alcohol. It has a fine cutting quality at the finish so should make an ideal foil for rich, fatty meaty foods. Seriously good buy.

8 The Best Côtes Catalanes 2015 £7.50

From the baking garrigue wilds of France's far southwest a rugged, spicy black-fruit gripper with the benefit of years; a savoury winter warmer; 14% alcohol.

8 The Best Red Burgundy 2016 £8.00

Vigorous strawberry-raspberry fruit from a 70/30 Pinot Noir/Gamay blend; fine ruby colour and convincing silky burgundian style; 13% alcohol.

10 Le Verdier Cairanne 2016 £10.00

A very grand Côtes du Rhône from star village appellation Cairanne, dark and savoury with coffee and spice depths to the perfectly poised and weighted rounded flavours made silkier with oak contact; miraculously good; the 15% alcohol doesn't daunt in the least.

9 The Best St Emilion 2015 £12.00

Plush, dense developed claret – exactly what you'd hope for at this sort of price; poised black fruits raised without oak contact but supple and smooth; 14% alcohol

RED WINES

FRANCE

8 **The Best Châteauneuf du Pape 2015 £14.00**
You'll only find this in 100 of the stores, but keep a lookout as it's good value for a maturing and relishably complex example of this pricy appellation; darkly ripe and spicy and 14% alcohol.

ITALY

9 **The Best Montepulciano 2016 £6.00**
This bushy-tailed vividly briary Abruzzo wine has plentiful red-berry fruit (many of these wines don't) and a keen nutskin-dry finish; 13% alcohol. Good partner for highly flavoured risotto and pasta dishes and a good price too.

9 **The Best Barbera d'Asti 2015 £6.50**
A good hit of crisp bramble fruit in this sprightly Piedmont red by Araldica; juicy and satisfying, 13.5% alcohol, and a pleasing partner for meaty-sauce pastas or grilled chops. Good price.

10 **Morrisons Nerello Mascalese 2016 £7.50**
Snazzy Sicilian in a screwcap bottle, from a grape very much at home on the (lower) slopes of the island's grumpy volcano, Etna. Nerello Mascalese is a lyrically named variety that makes distinctive regional reds typified by this everyday IGT example: purple and perky with violet and briar aromas, focused juicy blueberry-plum fruits and a gentle abrasion at the finish. A nifty match for full-flavoured fish dishes as well as pasta and meatier fare; 13.5%. Outstanding for interest and value.

RED WINES

ITALY

10 The Best Toscana 2015 £10.00

The Morrisons team are mighty proud of this one-off wine, developed with the San Felice winery in Chianti country. A 'supertuscan' blend largely of Chianti's Sangiovese with Cabernet and Merlot it has a clear cherry-cassis aroma and smooth dark savours of blackberry fruits and a proper nutskin dry finish; 13% alcohol. A sumptuous but superbly poised and thoroughly Italian wine – bravo!

8 The Best Amarone 2015 £15.00

If you like the souped-up Valpolicella style this is a decent one with a good dose of the *amarone* ('bitter') pungency that counterpoints the hefty ripeness; smooth, brooding and rich; 14.5% alcohol.

9 The Best Barolo 2012 £15.00

Enticing limpid colour with orange at the rim – a good sign of dignified age – and a sweet rose-petal aroma introduce this fine generic Barolo by big but dependable producer Araldica; sleekly lush with ripest red-berry fruits and a perfect crisp finish; 14% alcohol. Very fair value.

PORTUGAL

8 The Best Douro 2015 £8.00

Tried this at home. On first opening, it seemed slight and weedy, but in the glass this table red from the Port country bloomed and fattened out with the hoped-for dark fruits and minty spiciness that are the Douro trademarks; 14% alcohol. A remarkable transformation.

RED WINES

SOUTH AFRICA

8 **Alto Rouge 2014** £9.50

Blood-red big sweet blackcurranty vanilla-oaked with plenty of gravitas; plump but skilfully balanced and neatly dry at the edge; 14.5% alcohol. From Bordeaux grapes plus Shiraz, it's like a sort of prodigal claret.

SPAIN

8 **Three Houses GSM 2017** £5.00

Dare I call this Sangria wine? Garnacha, Syrah and Monastrell, it's really too good for slopping into punch. Sunnily ripe and juicy it finishes clean and lipsmacking; 12.5% alcohol.

9 **The Best Reserva Rioja 2013** £7.50

From ubiquitous Bodegas Muriel, a sleek cassis wine rounding out in healthy balance with the vanilla richness of the oak contact; 13.5% alcohol. Good price.

9 **The Best Priorat 2015** £10.00

This decidedly interesting contemplative wine from a cult Catalan backwater has gamey, spicy depths to the berry and briar fruit with a firm grip of savoury tannin; should evolve happily for years; 14.5% alcohol.

9 **The Best Gran Reserva Rioja 2012** £12.00

The blackcurrant thrill of the Tempranillo is still very bright in this super-silky wine by formidable Bodega Baron de Ley. Clearly the fruit will, as it should, stay ahead of the oak in the balance but my guess is this lovely wine needs more time in the bottle; invest now but try to be patient; 14% alcohol.

PINK WINES

ARGENTINA

8 **Vinalba Malbec Rosé 2018** £8.50

Shell pink, fresh floral nose, balanced red-berry refreshing fruit finishing brisk with an underlying healthy ripeness; 13% alcohol.

AUSTRALIA

8 **Workshop Bench Blend Rosé 2017** £5.75

Salmon (lightly poached) colour gives on to a generously fruity set of flavours formed by the quirky grape blend of Shiraz with southern Italian Negroamara and Aglianico. How about that? Very decent balanced dry pink of real interest; 14% alcohol. A food wine: will stand up to anything.

FRANCE

7 **Amalthée Provence Rosé 2017** £9.00

Pale shell pink colour, quite fresh, delicate and dry, and quite expensive; 13% alcohol.

ITALY

8 **Vitis Nostra Pinot Noir Rosé 2017** £7.00

Smoked-salmon colour, sweet cherry nose and discreet just-about-dry cherry-strawberry fruit; easy-going Venetian aperitif pink with 11.5% alcohol.

WHITE WINES

ARGENTINA

10 The Best Gran Montaña Reserva Chardonnay 2016 £9.00

Argentina's Uco Valley might not be the first place you'd look for standout Chardonnay but this team effort by Morrisons winemakers and local producer La Agricola has come up with something special. It's richly coloured, apple-strudel perfumed, part-oaked and beautifully poised; 13% alcohol. A new marker on the long, worldwide Chardonnay road.

AUSTRALIA

9 Workshop Bench Blend Pinot Grigio 2017 £5.75

It's part Riesling, which might explain the clear tang in the pineapple-perfumed orchard fruit; a good balance of fresh flavours and quite dry; 13% alcohol. At this price, way above average for PG interest and value from anywhere.

8 Jim Barry Watervale Riesling 2017 £14.00

Lime and lemon style to this big mineral Clare Valley wine will make it a grand match for special-occasion Asian menus; 12% alcohol.

FRANCE

8 The Best Touraine Sauvignon Blanc 2017 £7.50

This racy but not sharp grassy Loire wine has clear purity and a lemon twist; 13% alcohol.

WHITE WINES

FRANCE

8 **The Best White Burgundy 2016** £8.00

Fresh apple-cabbage salad of flavours in this creamy-ripe Mâconnais Chardonnay; 13% alcohol.

9 **The Best Vouvray 2016** £8.50

Honey aromas in the nose of this fine mineral Loire Chenin Blanc balancing waxy richness with lemon-lime acidity; these might sound contradictory elements, but it's entirely harmonious; 12% alcohol.

9 **The Best Petit Chablis 2017** £10.00

From the humblest of the Chablis appellations this wine by the leading co-operative La Chablisienne seems pretty grand to me. Elegant gunflint and lemon highlights in the sunny Chardonnay fruit and a keen acidity are in the classic Chablis style all the way; 12% alcohol.

9 **The Best Pouilly-Fumé 2017** £12.00

An exciting wine which seems to me the ideal 'expression' of this great Loire appellation's Sauvignon Blanc style: leafy blackcurrant aroma, river-pebble freshness, seagrass lushness, green but not tart acidity; fine balance and very dry; 13% alcohol.

WHITE WINES

FRANCE

9 **The Best Chablis Premier Cru 2013** **£15.00**

This slot was occupied last year by the much-lauded 2014 vintage, so this must be a holdover. It's bright and fresh with trademark flint and unexpected sherbet on the nose with a crafty richness from some oak-aged wine in the blend, retaining a fine balance between Chardonnay lushness and Chablis green acidity; 13% alcohol. Great stuff.

GERMANY

8 **Vom Löss Riesling Trocken 2016** **£8.00**

Emphatic green-apple perfume and matching crispness in the fruit of this racily stimulating Rheinpfalz dry aperitif; 13% alcohol.

ITALY

8 **The Best Fiano 2017** **£6.00**

A Sicilian spin on the pleasant theme of the ancient Fiano grape's trick of combining honey notes with nutty creaminess and grassy freshness; 13% alcohol.

9 **The Best Falanghina 2017** **£6.50**

This is the wine that stood out for me among a pretty good run of budget Italian whites on the day at Morrisons. It's a snappily dry Campania wine, crisply keen and refreshing for aperitif drinking; 13% alcohol.

WHITE WINES

ITALY

8 **The Best Vermentino 2017** £6.50

Crisp Sardinian dry white with fun brassica notes among the peach and pear, lemon and lime that make up the cheery salad of flavours; dry and bright and 12.5% alcohol. To me it says fish, salami, risotto.

8 **The Best Grillo 2017** £7.25

Crisp white orchard fruit laced with lemon and grapefruit in this eager Sicilian native varietal; 13% alcohol.

9 **Minea Greco di Tufo 2016** £10.00

The Greco is a grape variety said to have been brought to Italy zillions of years ago by immigrant ancient Greeks. In this Campania wine there is a kind of primordial earthy spiciness to the lemon-tinged orchard-fruit lushness and a relishable arcane deliciousness; 12.5% alcohol. Lobster would be nice.

MOLDOVA

8 **Morrisons Pinot Grigio 2017** £4.25

Genuine, fleetingly smoky, dry, orchard-fruit party wine with easy plumpness; 13% alcohol. Moldova, a landlocked former Soviet republic, celebrates 25 years of its new democratic constitution in 2019. It is the poorest country per capita in Europe and the least visited by tourists. Flock to Moldova! Drink the wines!

WHITE WINES

NEW ZEALAND

8 **The Best New Zealand Sauvignon Blanc 2017** £8.00

From the very busy Yealands Estate, the big fresh flavours include asparagus and sweet green pepper; acidity is crisp and there's a sly ripeness – a crowd pleaser; 13% alcohol.

SOUTH AFRICA

8 **The Best South African Sauvignon Blanc 2017** £6.50

Cape Sauvignon seems to me to compare progressively more favourably with its Kiwi counterpart, very often with a price advantage as well. This one's brisk, grassy and full of interest – and a bit of a bargain; 13% alcohol.

8 **The Best Chenin Blanc 2017** £7.00

The lavish colour is matched by lush ripe peachy-vegetal flavours and trace-of-nectar aroma, and all this forming a dry, fresh wine with crisp lime edge; 13.5% alcohol.

SPAIN

8 **The Best Albariño 2017** £7.00

Seaside fresh Rias Baixas wine with a good heft of grassy green fruit and citrus tang, plenty of interest; 12.5% alcohol. Competitive price for this sought-after style.

8 **The Best Rioja Blanco Reserva 2013** £13.00

Lavish gold colour and creamily perfumed old-fashioned new-oak-matured white Rioja in a gaudy livery; nostalgically lush and yet lively with it; 12.5% alcohol.

SPARKLING WINES

FRANCE

8 Adrien Chopin Champagne Brut **£18.00**

New to me, a blanc de noirs (all Pinots, no Chardonnay) with mellow colour and fruit with a sense of plenty of time in bottle; 12% alcohol.

8 The Best Champagne Brut **£19.00**

Made by Louis Kremer, there's a crusty-loaf aroma mixed into the lively lemony nose and long reassuring fruit in the rush of creamy bubbles; 12% alcohol.

ITALY

8 Maschio Prosecco Conegliano **£9.00**

Extra dry, it says on the label, but I thought it jolly sweet. Well, at least it's jolly in some sense, and my friend Brian liked it. Good of its kind is probably the best description; 11% alcohol.

Sainsbury's

Will it be renamed Sainsda's, or Asbury's? This was the searching question I hoped to address to the Sainsbury's team at this year's wine tasting, which coincided exactly with the shock announcement that this Great British Institution is to merge with Yankee-owned upstart Asda.

But the ever-cheerful and talented wine people at Sainsbury's had other priorities on the day. Nearly every wine in the line-up was from the own-label Taste the Difference range, and the team were anxious to show off the new vintages and the occasional new wine.

I must mention perennial pair Taste the Difference Languedoc Red and White, made for Sainsbury's by the extremely busy Jean-Claude Mas. His two 2017 wines, both retailing at just £7.00 (and nevertheless quite often individually discounted) are so good I've had to award my first-ever tandem maximum score. Neighbouring red Taste the Difference Pic St Loup 2016 also scores 10, and from not much further away, Taste the Difference St Chinian 2016 is equally impressive, uniquely delicious; I am only puzzled as to why I've scored it a mere 9.

And so on. Sainsbury's pretty-much invented own-label supermarket wine in the 1970s, and has maintained a strong lead in this highly competitive field ever since. There is no sign of flagging.

This certainly applies to the promotion of the wines. There are always plenty of individual wines on offer at useful discounts. The regular overall 25% off everything offers also continue with undiminished frequency and, it seems to me, always in coincidence with similar promos at Tesco. Long may this rivalry continue.

RED WINES

AUSTRALIA

10 **Taste the Difference Barossa Cabernet Merlot 2016** **£10.00**

This is no mere generic Barossa bruiser, but a slick production by senior estate Chateau Tanunda. It fits: colour veers to black, perfume is high-toned cassis, vanilla, even cigar box; it's sublimely savoury and lithe in its darkness of berry fruits, with the Merlot playing a clear role in plumping the Cabernet muscle; 14.5% alcohol. Try with roast beef – and no worries, this wine will cope comfortably with the horseradish sauce.

AUSTRIA

8 **Taste the Difference Zweigelt 2017** **£9.00**

This rare Austrian red has a shining crimson hue and intriguing wild-berry aroma with a hint of raisins; easy weight and balance with ripe brambly appeal; 13% alcohol. Worth trying straight from the fridge.

CHILE

8 **Diablo Dark Red 2015** **£12.00**

New brand from redoubtable Concha y Toro of Casillero del Diablo (Devil's Cellar) renown looks in its scarlet livery as if it might be overheated, but it's well-judged, evoking a luscious blackberry pie under a sweetly caremalised crust with cream on the side but brightly fruity and with a trim acidity; 13.5% alcohol.

FRANCE

8 **SO Organic Merlot 2016** **£6.50**

Healthy (appropriately, I suppose) modern claret, mostly Merlot, with a pleasing chocolate abrasion to the black berry fruit; dark and developed with 13.5% alcohol. Note the former organic label design with the elegant botanical vine illustration has been replaced by something less appealing.

RED WINES

FRANCE

10 Taste the Difference Languedoc Rouge 2017 £7.00

Another big, dark-maroon-coloured vintage for this perennial bargain from Mediterranean maestro Jean-Claude Mas. It's very ripe (13.5% alcohol) and gives off an encouraging tea-leaf tannin note on the nose; abundant juicy-spicy hedgerow fruits with raisiny intensities and a crafty plumpness from partial oak contact. It's by no means overpriced at £7.00, and is still regularly discounted to £6.00.

9 Domaine du Colombier Chinon 2016 £7.00

Superb new vintage of this terrific Loire perennial is grippingly good with its leafy-stalky abrasion to the bold redcurrant fruit and satisfying juicy heft; 12.5% alcohol. Don't hesitate to serve this distinctive wine cool, and enjoy with white meats, charcuterie, saucy fish dishes and more.

8 Les Calcaires Pinot Noir 2017 £7.00

From the Loire, where 'the fossil-rich, alkaline limestone soils impart their minerality to the wines', say Sainsbury's. Fair enough. I liked the pale cherry colour, sweet/stalky nose and crisp raspberry juiciness; 13% alcohol. Think of this as a brave attempt at the style of red Sancerre, and you're getting a bargain.

8 Taste the Difference Beaujolais Supérieur 2017 £7.50

Quite dark for Beaujolais, and quite noticeably ripe too, this has generous juicy bounce and rounded completeness not always found in the ordinary (well, all right, 'superior') wines; 13% alcohol.

RED WINES

FRANCE

10 Taste the Difference Pic St Loup 2016 £9.00

Worthy successor to the excellent 2015 vintage, it's warm with the dark spice and ripeness that mark out the best Languedoc reds, with thyme and briar featuring in the slinky Syrah-led fruit; 13% alcohol. Equally nifty match for roasted lamb or duck. In this vintage, Pic is a mere Languedoc appellation; from 2017 it will be promoted to Appellation Pic St Loup Protégée; a worthy award but price hikes might follow.

9 Taste the Difference St Chinian 2016 £9.00

A recent addition to Sainsbury's Languedoc list and miraculously good: full-force fruits-of-the-forest Syrah-Grenache blend with warming garrigue flavours of the sun-baked Mediterranean hinterland hills; has what I can only call the true St Chinian style (very much a personal favourite) with peppery power and wholesome heft; 14% alcohol. Screwtop and holds up very well for next-day finish.

8 Taste the Difference Côtes du Ventoux 2016 £10.00

Fine strong wine might be just a bit too ripe for some tastes. I felt a bit of scorch amid the peppery black-fruit flavours; 15% alcohol.

RED WINES

FRANCE

9 **Taste the Difference Château Les Bouysses Cahors 2015** **£10.75**

Smooth but grippy, rich and roasty pleasantly charred Malbec from the Lot Valley appellation still redolent of its long-extinct notoriety for 'black wine' is genuinely standout in style and a fine, spicy winter red; 13.5% alcohol. The constituent Malbec grape is prominently proclaimed on the label but in fact is known by another name, Cot, in this region. Word to the wise: finish this in one sitting. Reopened next day the wine remaining had oxidised – maybe thanks to the wide-bottomed shape of the posh bottle.

8 **Taste the Difference Gigondas 2015** **£14.00**

I am always anxious to taste Gigondas, the most propitious of the southern Rhône village appellations – and the most expensive. This is a good one: sweet seductive darkness of colour and blackberry aromas, silky ripe oaked texture and notes of violets, Mediterranean herbs and spicy savours; 14% alcohol. Lovely match for roasts.

GERMANY

9 **Taste the Difference Rheinhessen Pinot Noir 2016** **£7.50**

Don't listen to carpers who claim all supermarket wines are alike. This limpid, brilliant cherry-bright Rotwein (that's German for red wine) is crisply delicious and silky smooth all at the same time; a totally distinctive treat to serve chilled as an aperitif or with fish, fowl, pasta or just about anything; 12.5% alcohol.

RED WINES

ITALY

9 **Taste the Difference Primitivo 2017** £7.00

First thing to say is how well this humble IGT from Salento in Italy's deep south holds up overnight. Yummy sweet-plum, even prune, fruit makes a clean cut for sticky pasta and it loses none of its fresh vigour recorked – well, recapped – for finishing next day; 14% alcohol. Exceptional interest and value.

8 **Taste the Difference Barbaresco 2014** £11.00

Light in colour, this tea-and-cherry-scented young-tasting wine doesn't match the 'rich and powerful' description on the back label, but it does have the distinct savour of this rightly celebrated Piedmontese classic; 13.5% alcohol. Might well evolve nicely if kept a year or two.

PORTUGAL

8 **Taste the Difference Portuguese Lisboa Red 2016** £7.00

From Port grapes grown north of Lisbon, a dark and spicy red with a lick of toffee richness from oak ageing and plenty of eucalyptus savour; 13.5% alcohol. Nice match for grilled meats.

9 **Taste the Difference Douro 2015** £9.00

The 2015 was still current as I went to press; if you can find it, grab it – lovely maturing dark wine with porty richness and spicy, minty, plummy black fruits made by serious estate Quinta do Crasto; 14% alchol.

RED WINES

SOUTH AFRICA

8 **Mount Rozier Cinsault 2017** £7.00

Pale but interesting Stellenbosch wine with a likeable abrasion of lucid red fruits, very dry finishing but amicably ripe and generous; 14% alcohol. Cinsault is predicted to become a signature Cape grape: this wine bodes well for it.

8 **Taste the Difference South African Azana Red Blend 2017** £9.00

Great, big, ripe (14.5% alcohol) and cushiony Shiraz-based blend with sweet spice and luscious blackberry-pie richness which somehow contrives not to go over the top; a likeable match for big-flavoured meaty dishes, such as South Africa's own bobotie.

SPAIN

8 **Taste the Difference Cepa Alegro Rioja Reserva 2011** £8.50

Clear signal of vanilla is first off the nose of this cheerfully blackcurranty mature wine; fruit is still to the fore and it's plump and sweet in the mouth; 13.5% alcohol.

PINK WINES

FRANCE

8 **Winemakers Selection Les Jardiniers Côtes du Rhône Rosé 2017** £6.00

The pale copper colour looks good (and colour counts for a lot in rosé) and you get a discreet strawberry sweetness amid the freshness and keen acidity; 12.5% alcohol. The price is a further attraction (why is most rosé so weirdly expensive?).

PINK WINES

FRANCE

8 **Taste the Difference Touraine Rosé 2017** **£7.00**
Salmon-coloured curio from the Loire made mainly with Gamay (the Beaujolais grape) and Cabernet Franc (the Loire's mainstay red grape); it has plenty of positive red-fruit bounce and is very dry; 13% alcohol.

8 **Taste the Difference Côtes de Provence Rosé 2017** **£9.00**
Pale shell pink, cool fleetingly honeyed floral nose, discreet red-fruit flavours, dry with a citrus suggestion; identikit Provence pink, well-made; 12.5% alcohol.

8 **La Terrasse Rosé 2017** **£10.00**
Bright Mediterranean blend by ubiquitous Jean-Claude Mas, maker of Sainsbury's brilliant Languedoc Red and White, this has a bright, alluring colour and juicy, full, soft-summer-red-fruit juiciness; ripe and generous with good freshness and 13.5% alcohol. It also comes in a fun magnum (1.5l) size at £20.00.

NEW ZEALAND

8 **Oyster Bay Rosé 2017** **£10.00**
The colour of this pure Pinot Noir veers close to red and the same goes for the nicely poised typical sweet-sour Kiwi Pinot fruit; I liked it, perhaps because it is so unrosé-like; 13.5% alcohol.

PINK WINES

SPAIN

8 **Taste the Difference Viñedos Barrihuelo Rioja Rosado 2017** £7.50

Made largely from Rioja's Tempranillo grape and showing the trademark cassis juiciness of the red Rioja style nicely set in the bright pink colour with tangy, lemony freshness; 13% alcohol.

WHITE WINES

AUSTRALIA

9 **Taste the Difference Barossa Chardonnay 2017** £7.00

They've taken producer Chateau Tanunda's name off the label, but this is the same friendly bargain as before: peachy-lush part-oaked fruit with a fine natural minerality and citrus spike; great balance and 13% alcohol.

AUSTRIA

8 **Taste the Difference Austrian Riesling 2017** £8.00

Bracing, crisp and yet ripely appley dry Riesling with heady aromatics, this is a fine aperitif wine as well as an obvious match for Asian dishes; 12.5% alcohol.

8 **Taste the Difference Grüner Veltliner 2017** £8.00

This dependable annual is briskly dry in the modern manner, with the trademark preserved-fruit aromas that distinguish it as an aperitif wine and make it a good match for exotic and spicy menus; 12.5% alcohol.

FRANCE

10 **Taste the Difference Languedoc Blanc 2017** £7.00

A wondrously consistent perennial that I somehow missed last year, ideally poised between exotic ripeness and bright white-fruit flavours, leesy and long but tangily crisp; 13% alcohol. Top value and yet regularly discounted.

WHITE WINES

FRANCE

9 **Taste the Difference Côtes du Rhône Blanc 2016** **£7.00**

White Côtes du Rhône is a rare bird in the supermarket firmament, so this in-house rendering by regional giant Gabriel Meffre really stands out. It's a plushly peachy and likeably vegetal dry wine of sunny complexity nicely balanced with citrus zest; 12.5% alcohol.

8 **Taste the Difference Bordeaux Sauvignon Blanc 2017** **£7.00**

Bordeaux's traditional dry whites have been rather left behind in the Sauvignon Blanc boom. Here's a contender: elegant, pure, restrained, classic style with plenty of natural Sauvignon character; 12% alcohol.

8 **Plaimont Côtes de Gascogne 2017** **£7.50**

Zesty and bright Gers dry wine offering lots of fresh orchard fruit lushness en route to a limey flavour edge; 11.5% alcohol.

10 **Taste the Difference Pouilly Fumé 2017** **£13.00**

Is this the best expression of Sauvignon Blanc there is? From the Caves de Pouilly deep in the Loire, it's suitably river fresh, almost saline, in its intensity and jumping with grassy lushness; ineffably delicious and a match for anything I've tasted from the Loire (neighbouring Sancerre included) all year, it makes even its grandest New Zealand counterparts look clunky; 13% alcohol.

WHITE WINES

GERMANY

10 Dr L Riesling 2017 £7.00

Marvellously fresh, racy moselle from the ingenious Dr Ernie Loosen, a star in the firmament of German winemaking; this hardy perennial in an elegant blue bottle teams the lush apple sweetness of the Riesling grape with the mineral purity of flavour that so evokes the steep, slaty vineyards of the region, all at just 8.5% alcohol and at a very keen price. Top aperitif.

8 Taste the Difference German Pinot Blanc 2017 £7.00

Mosel spin on the theme of Alsace Pinot Blanc, a distinctive mix of aromatic and tangy with a little bit of white-nut creaminess; likeable herbaceous style with 12.5% alcohol. Pinot Blanc is usually called Weissburgunder in Germany.

ITALY

9 Taste the Difference Soave Classico 2017 £7.00

Beguiling gold-green colour and white-nut lemon-tang nose to this simple, fresh and typical Verona classic; 12% alcohol. Soave was cool in the 1970s, when wine was still esoteric and it's still, oddly enough, cool now.

8 Taste the Difference Pinot Grigio Trentino 2017 £7.00

I may have said this before, but if you insist on drinking Italian Pinot Grigio, it might as well be this one. It's from the sub-Alpine Trentino region, where higher altitude might just make for more suitable fruit, and you do get some of the smoke and aromatics that mark out proper PG in Alsace; it's full of fruit and pretty dry; 12.5% alcohol.

WHITE WINES

ITALY

8 **Taste the Difference Vernaccia di San Gimignano 2017** **£8.00**

Peculiar as it is to the famed Tuscan hill town, I wonder if this wine sells exclusively to people who have visited San Gimignano. Eschew the crowds and evoke the glories of the place by trying this briskly lemony refresher for its generous but tightly defined white fruits; 12.5% alcohol.

8 **Taste the Difference Gavi 2017** **£8.50**

Attractive pale gold colour, shy nose and entry then a shimmer of inviting, fresh white fruit suggesting nectarine and citrus along with and a blanched almond richness, all tangy and dry; 12.5% alcohol.

9 **Taste the Difference Vermentino 2017** **£9.00**

Vermentino is a staple white-wine grape of Corsica and Sardinia, but this one is from Salice Salentino in Puglia; alluring rich colour and inviting floral aromas lead on to ripe orchard-fruit flavours of real resonance; very likeable, very Italian dry white to match all sorts of pastas and fowl as well as fishy dishes; 12.5% alcohol.

9 **Taste the Difference Greco di Tufo 2017** **£10.00**

From vineyards at around 2,000 feet above sea level in the volcanic region of the Campania, a dry, complex wine with suggestions not just of the wild flora that flourish on the surface but of the primordial mineralities of what lies beneath; 12.5% alcohol. Very nicely presented, and a versatile food match even for assertive flavours.

WHITE WINES

PORTUGAL

8 **Taste the Difference Portuguese Alvarinho 2017** **£7.50**

A transparent attempt to exploit the craze for Spain's Rias Baixas Albariño, made just the other side of Portugal's northwest frontier, this has a steely nose and flavour with plenty of briny Atlantic freshness; a better bet than vinho verde; 12.5% alcohol.

SPAIN

8 **Taste the Difference Viñedos Barrihuelo Rioja Blanco 2017** **£7.00**

Modern (unoaked) dry white Rioja showing off constituent grape Viura's hot-house-peach-style ripeness and juiciness to good effect with a twang of citrus to balance; 12.5% alcohol.

9 **Taste the Difference Albariño Rias Baixas 2017** **£8.50**

Sainsbury's was first among the supermarkets on to the Albariño bandwagon a decade or more back, and this wine has been out front ever since. It's blowing a proper Atlantic breeze of tangy salinity but also delivering generously ripened grassy fruit and lemon zest; 13.5% alcohol.

SPARKLING WINES

FRANCE

8 **Taste the Difference Crémant de Loire Rosé** **£11.00**

Very lively 'brut' sparkler with a smoked-salmon hue and attractive strawberry whiff; fresh and crisp; not an imitation of champagne at all, but becoming fashionable, I am told; 12.5% alcohol.

SPARKLING WINES

FRANCE

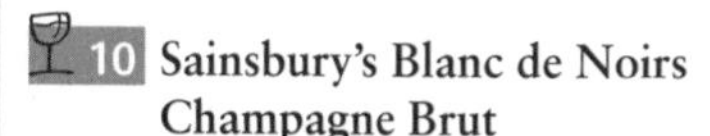

10 **Sainsbury's Blanc de Noirs Champagne Brut** **£18.00**

Yet another new presentation for this consistent house champagne includes a redesigned label in which the name Sainsbury's seems intentionally camouflaged; it's a well-coloured champagne, brioche in aroma, mellow and ideally balanced, and top value; 12.5% alcohol.

9 **Taste the Difference Demi-Sec Champagne** **£18.00**

'Demi-Sec' tends to summon up visions of Asti-Spumante-style sticky confections, but well-made DS champagne is a greatly undervalued treat. Good ones like this are only fractionally more 'sweet' (liquor-dosed at disgorgement) than 'brut' wines and have a mellowness all their own. If you don't like your champagne too green, do try this; 12% alcohol.

SPAIN

0 **Nosecco** **£3.75**

Any joke at the expense of Prosecco is fine with me, but this 0.5% alcohol damp squib from Spain's La Mancha is surely a tilt too far. No smell, no flavour, no point.

Spar

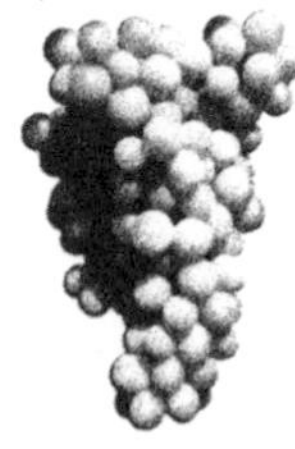

A new retailer on these pages, Spar is a 'voluntary food retail chain' with 2,700 member shops nationwide. Launched in Britain sixty years ago, Spar convenience stores are all independent and no two are exactly alike. But they all carry a great variety of Spar brands, including wine.

Lately, the wine offering has begun a notable transformation. The new ranges are sourced by Philippa Carr, a Master of Wine with much experience in the supermarket sector and, I reckon, an unrivalled nose for interest and value.

Among the recent introductions is an 'Alphabet' series labelled with the initials of their constituent grape varieties, all priced at £6. I have particularly liked the CS, a Cabernet Sauvignon from France's Languedoc, and G for Garnacha, from Spain's Castille. SB for Sauvignon Blanc, another wine from the Languedoc, stands out among the whites.

Completely new to me is the Regional Selection range. I suppose it's early days to be saying so, but I believe this is an outstanding collection. Mostly sourced from France and Latin America, they have a common thread of authenticity and sheer drinkability. Hard to pin down, I know, but I do think these wines, identified by decoratively bordered labels and a discreet gold-medal-style 'RS' symbol, form the best new in-house range I've tried in years.

RED WINES

ARGENTINA

Rios de los Andes Mendoza Malbec Regional Selection 2017 £6.50

Raspberry colour and matching soft-fruit perfume followed up by perky raspberry fruit all bright and balanced. But this isn't Pinot Noir, it's Malbec. Untypical maybe, but a likeable juicy red that will chill well and do very well at barbecues; 12.5% alcohol.

Rios de Los Andes Malbec Mendoza Reserva Regional Selection 2017 £8.00

And now, like the proverbial rabbit out of the hat, pops up a much more familiar Argentine Malbec in the shape of this reserve (maybe oak-aided) variation on its namesake above. Darker, heftier and more intense with spice and grip, but still with the same juicy raspberry charm; 13.5% alcohol.

CHILE

Valle de Maule Merlot Reserva Regional Selection 2017 £7.50

Sweet black-cherry nose, roasty-ripe corresponding dark fruit with giveaway Merlot choc'n'cherry savour; this is a cracker – Chilean Merlot through and through in rewarding balance; 13% alcohol.

Valle de Leyda Pinot Noir Reserva Regional Selection 2016 £7.50

There is a roasty savour to the plump summer red fruit in this recognisably ripe and evolved Chilean Pinot. The food-match suggestion of duck is spot on; 14% alcohol.

RED WINES

FRANCE

9 **CS Cabernet Sauvignon 2016** £6.00

From the strikingly labelled Alphabet own-brand range at Spar this Languedoc red stands out for solid colour, juicy cassis fruit and wholesome completeness; 12.5% alcohol.

9 **Côtes du Rhône Regional Selection 2017** £6.50

Agreeably spiky and abrading textbook 'everyday' CdR with intense colour and brimming with wild peppery red fruits. Fine assertive food red – roast or grilled meat, starchy dishes, hard cheeses – with 13.5% alcohol.

9 **Bordeaux AOP Regional Selection 2016** £7.50

Handsome ruby colour, alluring ripe but elegant blackberry/blackcurrant fruit aromas and a clear claret slinkiness make this a very ready charmer indeed. Nicely evolved and 13% alcohol.

8 **Legendary Malbec 2016** £7.50

Friendly vigorous brambly Comte Tolosan wine to drink with starchy dishes and pongy cheese; 12% alcohol.

8 **Costières de Nîmes Fontaines du Sud 2016** £8.00

Well-defined raspy-spicy red-fruit wine from a distinctive Rhône appellation; has an easy weight and bright, juicy style but is none the less substantial and comforting in style; nicely presented food red – sausages, pork chops, starchy dishes – at a legitimate price; 13% alcohol.

ITALY

8 **Villa Cerro Valpolicella Ripasso 2016** £10.00

The distinctive redcurrant and pomegranate tang of Verona's juicy lightweight Valpolicella comes through brightly in this agreeably plumped-up speciality red; really nicely contrived pasta matcher with 13% alcohol and proper grippy finish.

RED WINES

ROMANIA

8 **Brindle Ridge Merlot 2017** £6.50

Bright crimson colour and bright fruit too in this model Merlot of distinct black-cherry character with just the right cherry bitterness as well; a dry middleweight wine with real charm; 13% alcohol.

8 **Wildflower Pinot Noir 2017** £6.50

The cherry colour just north of rosé takes you into a Beaujolais-like red-fruit lightweight refresher that artfully balances cherry-raspberry sweetness with clean acidity; an attractively presented wine to drink chilled with charcuterie, pizza and the like; 12.5% alcohol.

SOUTH AFRICA

8 **Breedekloof Pinotage Regional Selection 2017** £6.50

Textbook Pinotage has smokiness to the pungent blueberry fruit and plenty of comforting darkness in its inky but balanced heft. Jolly good of its kind and keenly priced; 14.5% alcohol.

SPAIN

8 **G Garnacha 2016** £6.00

The roasty ripeness to this Castilian heavyweight (14.5% alcohol) is well counterpointed by its gentle grip of tannin; red-meat red with gentle spice and plenty of forward black fruit.

WHITE WINES

CHILE

9 **Leyda Sauvignon Blanc Regional Selection 2017** £7.50

Very likeable grapefruit pungency shines through the exotic ripeness of this trademark Chilean Sauvignon; lots of refreshment and interest in the big green-fruit flavours; 12.5% alcohol.

8 **Valle de Casablanca Chardonnay Reserva Regional Selection 2017** £7.50

Safe but by no means unexciting cool-climate varietal has lively crisp-apple aromas and lush-but-crunchy matching fruit flavours all in nifty balance; lick of richness; 13% alcohol.

FRANCE

9 **SB Sauvignon Blanc 2017** £6.00

Big tangy perfume lures you into this lively Languedoc wine in the Alphabet series, made in a style I'll dare to compare to the Kiwi method: gooseberry-piquant, grassy and nettly. It's fresh and uplifting, and a bargain at this price; 12% alcohol.

8 **Tino Pai Sauvignon Blanc 2017** £7.00

With its Polynesian-style name and ethnically interesting graphic label design this is surely pretending to be from New Zealand. But it's a basic vin de France made by respectable Loire Valley outfit Lacheteau, and a respectable effort, too, at imitating the fruit-led, full-flavour Kiwi Sauvignon style. I'm confused by the catholicism but like the plump, grassy, green-pepper style well enough; 11.5% alcohol.

WHITE WINES

FRANCE

7 **Jean-Marie Garnier Chardonnay 2017 £7.00**
Soft vin de France; tropical-fruit style, dry but not overendowed with balancing acidity; needs to be served very cold; 12.5% alcohol.

9 **Bourgogne Chardonnay Regional Selection 2016 £9.00**
Crikey, this is good. You get the instant thrill of burgundy recognition with the first whiff of peachy-pineapple lushness underlined with creaminess and minerality. And that's all before the first sip, which certainly follows through fully. Lovely luxury dry wine, Mâconnais I'd guess, at a sensible price; 12% alcohol.

ITALY

9 **Grillo Sicilia Regional Selection 2017 £6.00**
Lime and lemon aromas positively bounce from this delightfully refreshing dry wine from the suitably citrussy island of Sicily. It's vividly fresh, with crisp orchard fruit beguilingly enriched with a sunny mango ripeness in its midst; 13% alcohol. Nifty match for creamy pasta and veggie dishes as well as fish and as an aperitif.

8 **Pinot Grigio Vigneti Dolomiti Regional Selection 2017 £7.00**
The grassy nature of the crisp pear fruit in this keen fresh spin on the perpetual PG theme sets it above the mean; 12.5% alcohol.

WHITE WINES

NEW ZEALAND

8 **Fern Hills Sauvignon Blanc Regional Selection 2017** £7.00

Big-flavoured Marlborough wine; has agreeable asparagus aromas and grassy vigour; 12% alcohol.

ROMANIA

8 **Brindle Ridge Chardonnay** £6.50

Non-vintage non-specific generic Chardonnay turns out well: ripe-looking colour, agreeable sweet-apple varietal nose and an artfully balanced fruit-freshness combo of peachy fruit and elusive creaminess with citrus crispness at the edge; 13% alcohol and nicely done.

7 **Wildflower Pinot Grigio 2017** £6.50

What to expect from Romanian Pinot Grigio? This melon-scented, grapefruit-evoking, approachable off-dry wine owes more to the Pinot Gris style of Alsace than to the everyday PGs of the Veneto, which is a plus; 12% alcohol.

SOUTH AFRICA

9 **Breedekloof Chenin Blanc Regional Selection 2017** £6.50

Hallmark citrus/honey formula pops up delectably in this well-coloured Cape Chenin. It's a dry wine but rich in peachy-nectary nuance, lush and long and yet keenly refreshing and stimulating; 13.5% alcohol. Seems underpriced.

SPARKLING WINES

FRANCE

8 **Marquis de Belrive Champagne Brut** **£17.50**
New champagne to me is made by Chanoine (est 1730 in Reims and now owned by Lanson) and makes a very welcome discovery. It's delicate and gently mellow with a crisp peary freshness; reassuring and supple; 12.5% alcohol.

ITALY

7 **Esprello Spumante Rosato Brut** **£6.50**
Party pink fizz; very pale and because it's fermented out to 11.5% alcohol really quite dry but with an underlying grapey sweetness; cheap but not nasty, to drink very cold.

8 **Prosecco Vino Spumante Extra Dry** **£7.50**
Smart bottle with a bright blue shield-shaped label which should stand out from the crowd; it really is a dry wine, not wildly fizzy (suits me) but popping with brisk bright orchard fruit in healthy balance; 11% alcohol.

8 **Prosecco Valdobbiadene Superiore** **£10.00**
Attractively presented premium Prosecco is, as proclaimed on the label, extra dry and indeed bordering on the austere with its steely style and crisp white fruit; much more interesting than average, with lively mousse; 11.5% alcohol.

Tesco

Tesco really is back. Profits have rebounded and the Booker takeover has been effected in 2018, adding muscle to Tesco distribution. There's talk that Booker-owned retailers Budgens and Londis might soon carry Tesco brands – including wine. And I like the press rumours that Tesco is secretly planning its own discounter chains to rival Aldi and Lidl.

Can't wait! But in the meantime, thanks to the most comprehensive tasting hosted by Tesco in a long while (the giant has, after all, just come out of a three-year sulk), I have been able to catch up on the wines.

They're great, and as before, it's the Finest own-label range that carries the flag. Mid-price reds from Bordeaux and Burgundy are particularly impressive but my highest score has gone to a Languedoc Malbec at just £5 – which was run a close second by Finest Argentinian Malbec at the same price.

Italy is strong this year. The Finest Barolo 2013 is excitingly good and I very much liked the Finest 2009 Chianti Classico – it's rare to find anything from the region of this age, especially at only eight quid a bottle. I have top-scored Finest Viña Cura Rioja Gran Reserva 2011 and hope it doesn't run out too soon. Likewise the terrific 2013 Reserva wine; I tasted the 2014, and it isn't as exciting, but might be in time.

Top whites include my favourite Chablis of the year, Finest Premier Cru 2016 – at £14 mind you – and perennial wonder Finest St Mont from the Pyrenees at just £6.

Finest Premier Cru Champagne is as brilliant as ever but they've radically altered the design of the label. Why do this? Is it a coincidence that Sainsbury's this year has also revamped the label of its house champagne? And is it a coincidence that whenever Sainsbury's does a 25% off six bottles promo Tesco follows suit? Oh all right, it might be the other way round. And let's hope they both keep it up.

RED WINES

ARGENTINA

9 **Finest Argentinian Malbec 2017** £5.00

You get more than your money's worth with this big sweetly ripe blackberry bumper but balanced 90% Malbec with lively juiciness smoothed with oak contact; 13% alcohol.

9 **Finest Trilogy Malbec 2015** £12.00

Maroon-black colour, delicious savour of briar, smoky black fruits and vanilla creaminess add up to a substantial treat from leading Menoza producer Catena; 13.5% alcohol.

AUSTRALIA

8 **Tesco Limestone Coast Merlot 2017** £6.00

Artful black-cherry style to a sweetly ripe but grippy-edged barbecue red; attractive and decent value; 14% alcohol.

8 **Finest McLaren Vale GSM 2015** £8.00

GSM as we're all supposed to know stands for Grenache, Shiraz and Mourvèdre, three of the key grapes for the blends of the Rhône and now for South Australia too. And this fine healthy red by Chester Osborn of d'Arenberg could even be a Rhône wine, so nicely defined and balanced as it is; 14.5% alcohol.

9 **Finest Barossa Shiraz 2016** £10.00

Midnight colour and piquant toasty-savoury perfume take you into a fine sleek intense and long flavour stream finishing grippingly complete; 14% alcohol; good value for this sort of quality and interest.

RED WINES

AUSTRALIA

8 **Finest Yarra Valley Pinot Noir 2017** **£11.00**
Maroon sweetly grapey- and pippy-smelling pure varietal is unmistakably Pinot Noir but nothing like the red burgundy it may or may not seek to replicate; it's so ripe there's a raisiny hint, but it's juicy, wild and fresh just the same; 13% alcohol.

FRANCE

9 **Tesco Côtes du Rhône 2016** **£4.30**
Spot-on CdR for silly money is spicily savoury – nice white-pepper note – and juicily lipsmacking; middleweight but full of focused fruit; 13% alcohol.

8 **Tesco Claret 2016** **£4.75**
More-than passable generic claret, 'healthy and balanced', it says in my note, adding purple for the colour, light for either the weight or the sense of illumination, not sure which; 12.5% alcohol. Price is a further lure.

8 **Tesco Beaujolais 2016** **£5.00**
Very decent purple-ripe and juicy number still seems in vigorous youth. The 2017 vintage, down in quantity but up (I'm told) in quality should be along soon.

10 **Tesco French Malbec 2017** **£5.00**
The Languedoc vineyards that supply the raw material for this wine lost 80% of the 2017 harvest to an apocalyptic April frost. But here's the wine just the same. Dense maroon colour, masses of juicy blackberry Malbec fruit stretched with 15% Cabernet Sauvignon. Maybe it's the Cabernet that makes it such a deliciously complete and superbly balanced wine; 11.5% alcohol. Heroic bargain.

RED WINES

FRANCE

Tesco

9 **Finest Médoc 2016** £8.20

Darkly dense colour and darkly ripe fruit in this immediately impressive Merlot-led Bordeaux; 'aspiring', I've called it in my note, trying to convey that it lives up to the 'Grand Vin de Bordeaux' motto on the label, even though it's unoaked; plush and rounded; 13% alcohol.

8 **Domaine L'Autrandine 2015** £9.00

Spice and liquorice lurk in the depths of this whoppingly ripe Côtes du Rhône's well-developed flavours; 14.5% alcohol.

8 **Finest Montagne Saint-Emilion 2016** £9.00

Concentrated maroon colour, bright blackberry aroma and a matching juicy fruit wrapped in soft tannin and tasting developed and slinky; 13.5% per cent.

9 **Finest Minervois La Livinière 2015** £9.50

Slinky, minty, theatrically dark-coloured and flavoured Languedoc cult wine evoking intense plum, liquorice and vanilla all in very reliable balance; a fine winter wine for rich stews and spicy savours; 13.5% alcohol.

8 **Finest Bourgogne Hautes Côtes de Nuits 2014** £12.00

Sleek cherry-red-berry juicy Pinot Noir aromas and flavours in this pale but plump and fleetingly creamy (some new oak) elegant burgundy; 12.5% alcohol. Convincing.

RED WINES

FRANCE

 9 **Finest 'Selection Georges' Mercurey 2014** **£13.00**

Vivid and defined Chalonnais (southern Burgundy) wine with an enticing sappy-earthy quality and a kind of crispness to the raspberry-cherry fruit; silky, developed and satisfying; 12.5% alcohol.

 9 **Château L'Estran Cuvée Prestige Médoc 2010** **£16.00**

Really grand mature wine from a great Bordeaux vintage; dark and hefty, full of cassis and cedar savour in the prescribed manner, and a proper treat for a special occasion; 13.5% alcohol.

8 **Finest Margaux 2014** **£20.00**

Absolutely legitimate de luxe claret from classed-growth Margaux estate Château Boyd Cantenac, already brimming with sweet briar aromas and fruit, sleeked with new-oak vanilla and grippingly taut, but it needs years to develop to its full potential; 13.5% alcohol. This is déclassé wine not the 'Grand Vin' made for bottling under the Château label, but it's delectable just the same, and about half the price.

ITALY

8 **Tesco Sicilian Rosso 2017** **£4.25**

Simple perky brambly blend made mainly from non-indigenous Syrah and Merlot; has neat dry edge for pizza nights; 12% alcohol.

9 **Finest Montepulciano d'Abruzzo 2016** **£6.50**

Brambly charm balanced by correcting crisp dryness makes this a vivid refresher to drink cool with pasta and pizza; very good of its kind; 13.5% alcohol.

RED WINES

ITALY

Tesco

8 Finest Lambrusco Reggiano £7.00
Authentic, dry, bitter-cherry Emilia-Romagna gently fizzy red for drinking well-chilled; 8% alcohol. Very slightly sweeter than some other brands.

9 Finest Chianti Classico Riserva 2009 £8.00
Remarkable to find a Chianti of this longevity, and it's very much alive with juicy cherry-blackcurrant fruits and lingering tannin to complete the balance; 13.5% alcohol. I believe it's a bargain.

8 Finest Aglianico 2015 £9.00
Fine dark mature Campania wine with black fruit and a hint of brimstone (by which I don't mean overdone sulphur, but a certain spicy-roasty relish) and oak-enriched long savours; 13.5% alcohol. A caveat though: the bottle I half-finished at home was dismally oxidised on the day after.

9 Sette Muri Brindisi Riserva 2014 £10.00
Standout bumper red from Adriatic province making particularly spicy wines from Negroamaro grapes; some are a bit tough and tannic but this is relishably ripe and balanced and full of interest; 14% alcohol. Comes in a very handsome, and very heavy bottle.

9 Finest Barolo 2013 £16.00
Very attractive limpid copper-ruby colour turning ochre at the edge and textbook tar-and-roses aroma lead into lovely slinky and evolved fruit with notes of coffee and sweet nut, a shade of spiritousness and seductive heft; 14% alcohol.

RED WINES

NEW ZEALAND

8 **Finest Marlborough Pinot Noir 2017** **£8.50**
Pale cherry colour and matching aroma, unoaked friendly midweight to drink cool with barbecued chicken – or prawns, mate. Quite sweet, if that's your taste; 13% alcohol.

9 **Finest Hawke's Bay Syrah 2016** **£10.00**
Savoury and fleetingly spicy dark blackberry fruit has the minty lift of the Kiwi style, making this a distinctively delicious discovery, quite unlike Aussie Shiraz (same grape, different name) and a versatile match for sausages, pies and other naughty delights; 13% alcohol.

9 **Finest Central Otago Pinot Noir 2016** **£12.50**
Healthy intense colour, welcoming raspberry nose, juicy and concentrated raspberry fruit with a lick of oak and a friendly grip at the finish; 13.5% alcohol. Made by Villa Maria. Proper food Pinot: roast birds, fish pie.

SPAIN

8 **Tesco Rioja 2017** **£4.50**
Under the Viña del Cura brand but not from the same maker as the Reserva Viña del Cura, a crimson young pure Tempranillo with ripe cassis nose and plump raspberry juiciness; 13% alcohol. Charming and cheap.

9 **Finest Viña del Cura Rioja Reserva 2013** **£8.50**
Lately repackaged but entirely consistent creamily-oaked, vigorously blackcurranty smoothie already nicely rounded out but probably with years ahead of it; modern, dependable Rioja from modern, dependable bodega Baron de Ley; 13.5% alcohol.

RED WINES

SPAIN

8 **Finest Viña del Cura Rioja Reserva 2014 £8.50**

This will succeed the formidable 2013, but seems less substantial and seductive; 13.5% alcohol. Of course it might develop in the bottle over time, but seek out the 2013 for as long as you can find any.

10 **Finest Viña del Cura Rioja Gran Reserva 2011 £11.00**

Gran Reserva Riojas have to be aged two years in cask then three in bottle before release and this one amply demonstrates the benefits. Deep ruby colour going gently orange at the rim, the nose is sweetly, tantalisingly ripe and the fruit near-chocolatey in its cassis intensity; the vanilla richness is in fine harmony; 14% alcohol. Best-value Gran Reserva of the day.

PINK WINES

SPAIN

8 **Tesco Garnacha Rosé 2017 £4.30**

Magenta Aragon wine; briskly briary and dry; fresh and lively; 13.5% alcohol.

WHITE WINES

AUSTRALIA

8 **Finest McLaren Vale/Adelaide Hills SR 2017 £8.00**

From renowned d'Arenberg winery an unexpected blend of Sauvignon and Riesling makes an agreeably nuanced orchard-fruit-citrus combo to match awkward menus from salads to assertive fish dishes; 12.5% alcohol.

WHITE WINES

AUSTRALIA

8 Finest Tingleup Riesling 2017 £8.50

From Australia's southwesternmost corner, a dry, limey and substantial mineral wine with a lot of heart; 12% alcohol. Suits Asian cooking.

8 Finest Yarra Valley Chardonnay 2016 £11.00

Controlled cool creaminess from oak contact lends luxury to this nicely extracted and healthy dry wine; 12.5% alcohol. Definitely the wine to go with prawns from the barbie.

CHILE

9 Concha y Toro Marques Casa Concha Chardonnay 2016 £12.50

Plush barrel-fermented pure varietal has clear aspirations to the Burgundy style and succeeds pretty well; creamy vanilla from (some) new oak enriches rather than overwhelms the peachy-sweet-pear fruit and there's a shaft of steeliness here too; ripe (14% alcohol) and artfully balanced, by Chile's astoundingly consistent giant Concha y Toro. Look out for regular discount. I paid £9.00 online.

FRANCE

10 Finest Saint Mont 2016 £6.00

Generous in colour, floral perfumes and fruit-salad flavours (spot the grapefruit) this Pyreneean perennial by the brilliant Plaimont co-operative is as delightfully fresh, fascinating and fulfilling as ever – and I note that the last vintage I described here was the 2012 thanks to Tesco's very patchy tasting opportunities. Highly distinctive dry wine with 12.5% alcohol and weirdly cheap.

WHITE WINES

FRANCE

9 **Finest Côtes de Gascogne 2017** £6.50

From excellent Plaimont co-op (makers of the fab St Mont above) a zingy refresher bursting with crunchy orchard fruit flavours and citrus twang; very dry, just short of green, excitingly fresh; 11.5% alcohol.

8 **Domaine des Bouts 2015** £9.00

This is a white Côtes du Rhône Villages, full of colour, sweet perfume and ripe tropical fruits with a richness that made me think of buttery scrambled eggs; made without oak contact, it's quite dry, and intriguingly good; 13.5% alcohol.

9 **Finest Viré-Clessé 2016** £11.00

This polished Mâconnais Chardonnay by big Burgundy outfit Bouchard Aîné has hallmark sweet-apple fruit with a trace of redcurrant, a fleeting richness (some of the wine was aged in new oak casks) and racy lemony acidity to balance; 12.5% alcohol.

10 **Finest Premier Cru Chablis 2016** £14.00

Gold-shot-with-green is the descriptive cliché for the colour and even the character of Chablis. This lovely wine conforms exactly. The Chardonnay fruit is ideally ripe and mineral-clear, the perfume is textbook and there is a wicked richness enhanced by time on the lees and in oak casks too; 13% alcohol.

ITALY

8 **Tesco Trebbiano d'Abruzzo 2017** £4.00

Identikit Italian dry white from the national grape has appley-lemon top flavours over almondy ripeness, brightly edged and clean; 12.5% alcohol. Party white at a mystifyingly low price.

WHITE WINES

ITALY

8 **Tesco Orvieto Classico 2017** £5.00

Secco style is floral on the nose, certainly dry but with a trace of white nut and an easy freshness; 12.5% alcohol.

9 **Finest Passerina 2017** £6.50

Abruzzo dry white from rare local grape, has sunny colour and matchingly ripe but mineral fruit with underlying white-nut creaminess; 13% alcohol; attractive match for pasta and risotto as well as fish and white meats.

8 **Finest Pecorino 2017** £6.50

Full-flavoured Abruzzo dry wine mixing a citrus twang with juicy white fruits; 13% alcohol.

8 **Finest Greco Beneventano 2016** £9.00

Autumn colour and fruits in this charismatic Campania grown-up's wine; its fruit is very ripe, even soft, but lifted by good acidity. A fine contemplative aperitif as well as a natural match for savoury fish and white-meat recipes or strong cheeses.

NEW ZEALAND

8 **Wairau Cove Pinot Grigio 2017** £6.50

Unconnectable to the Italian style of Pinot Grigio, this has a cushiony plumpness of orchard fruit (soft Williams pear pops into the mind) stiffened by bright citrus freshness and an underlying smoky suggestion; 13% alcohol.

8 **Wairau Cove Sauvignon Blanc 2017** £7.00

Crowd-pleaser combining prickly-nettly green fruit with a crafty sweetness in an attractive balancing act; 12% alcohol.

WHITE WINES

NEW ZEALAND

8 **Finest Marlborough Riesling 2016** £8.00

Minty-cool, tart-appley and limey with a neat note of sweetness at the finish, a welcome example of the unique style of Kiwi Riesling; 11.5% alcohol.

9 **Finest Gisborne Chardonnay 2016** £9.00

Kiwi Chardonnay is elusive these days, so here's a timely reminder of what we've been missing. This is part new-oak fermented, dry and appley-peachy in style, eggy-rich but quite flintily mineral and definitely distinctive; 13% alcohol. Like it? Love it.

SOUTH AFRICA

8 **Finest South African Chenin Blanc 2017** £7.00

Dry but not austere Breede River pure varietal with lemony notes over the crisp fruit and a background trace of Chenin honey; 12.5%. Wholesome vivid wine made under the Fairtrade scheme.

8 **Bellingham The Bernard Series Chenin Blanc 2016** £12.50

Extraordinary Cape wine, gold in colour with a whiff delectably reminiscent of petrolly old Riesling; matured in a mix of new and nearly new oak casks, it's extravagantly rich but vivid with classic nectar-lemon Chenin fruit; 14% alcohol. Shellfish and smoked salmon come to mind as matches.

SPAIN

8 **Tesco Viña del Cura Rioja Blanco 2017** £5.00

Simple, fresh, lemon-edged dry wine of natural weight made without oak contact; 12.5% alcohol.

WHITE WINES

SPAIN

8 **Finest Viña del Rey Albariño 2017** **£8.00**

Really quite a bracing and assertive style to this Rias Baixas wine by Spanish giant Felix Solis. Briny intense white fruit will nicely partner shellfish and smoked fish but might overwhelm your prawn cocktail; 12.5% alcohol.

FORTIFIED

SPAIN

9 **Finest Aged Fino Sherry 37.5cl** **£6.00**

Made by Gonzalez Byass of Tio Pepe renown, a tinglingly tangy very pale dry sherry with huge aromatic pungency and truly sharpening freshness; fabulously good to drink very well-chilled; 15% alcohol.

8 **Finest Cream Sherry 37.5cl** **£6.00**

Another Gonzalez Byass wine, this has a tawny amontillado hue, fine honey-citrus aroma and a friendly balance of pungent fruit with silky raisiny sweetness; 18% alcohol. Like drier sherries, served it chilled.

SPARKLING WINES

FRANCE

8 **Finest 1531 Blanquette de Limoux 2015** **£9.99**

Same good vintage as last year and none the worse for it, this is a dry but generous full-fizz bottle-fermented sparkler with mellow flavours and lifting acidity; 13% alcohol. The 1531 in the name is the date the monastery at Limoux first made the forbear of this wine – more than a century before sparkling wine was invented (in England).

SPARKLING WINES

FRANCE

9 **Finest Premier Cru Champagne Brut** **£19.00**

Same excellent non-vintage house champagne exclusively from rated Premier Cru vineyards but under a radically redesigned label. The colour may be a little more golden than of memory and there's the keynote bakery aroma, busy tiny-bubble mousse and mellow mainly Chardonnay fruit, lively, bright and satisfying; 12.5%. I've seen half bottles at a reasonable £11.00.

9 **Finest Vintage Grand Cru Champagne 2012** **£25.00**

I've heard it said that 2012 is the best year for single-vintage champagne since 2008, and there's a clue in this fine lemon-topped pure-Chardonnay new from Tesco at what seems a very fair price. It tasted long and lovely on the day, and it will surely develop very well. My tip is to wait for the next 25% off any six or more wines in-store offer and invest for a very fortuitous future; 12.5% alcohol.

ITALY

8 **Finest Prosecco Valdobbiadene Brut** **£10.00**

An oddity about this handsomely presented prestige Prosecco is that it includes 15% Chardonnay in with the formula grape Glera. It's softly frothy in the usual way, not dry enough to be the claimed 'brut' in style but quite appealing in its fizzy elderflower-pear fruitiness; 11.5% alcohol.

Waitrose

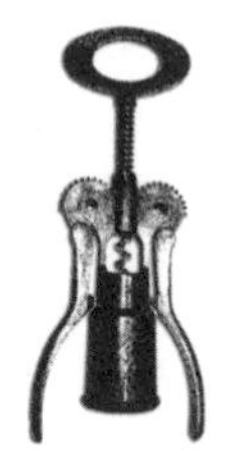

Let's get this straight at once. Waitrose is the supermarket with the best range of wines. By a country mile. Nobody else comes close. But Waitrose is expensive, right? Well no. It isn't. Not for wine anyway. The listed shelf prices, where they are directly comparable with rivals, are bog-standard.

But that's not the half it. Great numbers of Waitrose wines are on promotion at any one time, typically with prices cut by a quarter or even a third. No strings. You don't have to buy six to qualify. Mind you, Waitrose does give you five per cent off if you do buy any six bottles at one go.

If there seem an awful lot of wines scoring 9 and 10 in this entry it's because there are. Out of 200 or so tasted at Waitrose as well as those tried at home I have enthusiastic notes on way over half of them. I have had to ration the overall number included here, and it is fair to say the quality runs deep.

France, unsurprisingly, is the source of most of my top scores at Waitrose this year. Max points go to a new Beaujolais made jointly by burgundy buyer Nick Room with Louis Jadot, and to a fabulous generic burgundy curiously named 'Mischief and Mayhem'. Chateau de Montfort Vouvray 2017 from the Loire, meantime, is my Chenin Blanc of the year in what really has been a great Chenin Blanc year all round.

While all the other supermarkets have been building up their own-label wines, Waitrose has to date merely toyed with a few, quirky one-offs under the barely discernible 'Waitrose in Partnership' banner and a handful of entry-level own brands. Now comes the Waitrose Blueprint series. There are already 39 wines, all bearing thematic blue labels, and ranging in price from £5.99 to £8.99. There are a few useful half bottles too. I have tasted a number of them, and the signs are good.

Don't overlook Waitrose's dedicated online wine service waitrosecellar.com. You can order all the wines (I think there are about 1500) on sale in the stores and quite a few that are not.

Waitrose

RED WINES

ARGENTINA

8 Waitrose Blueprint Malbec 2017 £7.99

Waitrose is coy about who makes this Mendoza wine, but it's one to be proud of: lively, squishy-but-smooth hedgerow-fruit flavours firmly edged and finishing long; 12.5% alcohol. There's also a half bottle at £4.49.

8 Santa Julia Malbec 2017 £9.39

From dependable Mendoza family Zuccardi, this unoaked wine already has a nicely rounded completeness to its supple black fruit; 13% alcohol.

9 Viñalba Reserve Malbec 2014 £13.99

Premium pure varietal from Patagonia has a standout sweet-spice savour to its pure piquant black cherry-berry fruit; creamy oak mantle and 14% alcohol. A clue to its elegant poise: it's made by a family lately arrived from Bordeaux.

AUSTRALIA

8 Irvine Merlot 2017 £7.99

Jim Irvine is immortalised as Australia's King of Merlot (it says here) and this Barossa wine is testament to it: friendly whack of poised morello fruit upfront, perkily pure and berry bright right through; 14% alcohol. Recommended by Waitrose with sausages, mash and rich gravy.

8 Rolf Binder Cabernet Sauvignon/ Merlot 2016 £13.99

Impressive lush but elegant Bordeaux-style Barossa blend, hefty but poised and deliciously evocative of the cassis and chocolate cherry characters of its constituents; 13.5% alcohol.

RED WINES

CHILE

8 **Waitrose Blueprint Reserva Carmenère 2016** **£7.49**

Actually, I didn't taste the 2016 because the sample didn't turn up on the day, but the 2015 was there, and so beguiling I must urge Carmenère fans to take a punt; 14% alcohol.

8 **De Martino Cinsault 2016** **£11.99**

Remarkably pale varietal from the Itata Valley, notorious for its high rainfall, but where it must be sunny too as this is generously ripe with herbaceous red fruits and a firm grip; 12.5% alcohol. A fine match for white meats and poultry.

FRANCE

9 **Cuvée Chasseur 2017** **£5.49**

The price has finally been carried past the £5 frontier and they've changed the label but this substantial Hérault Carignan-Grenache remains an out-and-out bargain: juicy but spicy and firm; 12% alcohol.

9 **Remy Ferbras Ventoux 2016** **£7.99**

After giving this same 2016 wine a curmudgeonly 8 points last year, I've tasted it again (it's still, inexplicably, in stock) and must raise the ante. Dense, brambly, peppery nose and concentrated savoury dark spicy fruit now nicely developed with bottle age; 14% alcohol.

8 **Esprit des Trois Pierres Costières de Nîmes 2016** **£8.79**

Crackingly good, dark blackberry-briar, warmly ripe Mediterranean meat-matcher – good with starchy bean dishes too as it has a nice 'cut' of acidity – with vigour and savoury abrasion; 13.5% alcohol. The Costières de Nîmes style is distinctive, if hard to nail down, and this definitely has it.

RED WINES

FRANCE

9 Jean-Luc Baldès Malbec du Clos Cahors 2015 **£8.99**

Back in the day, you didn't need to tell punters Cahors was made from Malbec (actually called Cot locally) but now the grape is more celebrated than the appellation, so needs must. That said, this is a heroic plummy-nosed and spicily savoury Cahors more than worthy of the name; 13.5% alcohol. Bargain at this price.

8 Les Nivières Saumur 2016 **£9.49**

This handsome crunchy Loire Cabernet Franc has sleek purple raspy-leafy fruit of real distinction to drink cool; 12.5% alcohol.

9 Château Pey La Tour 2015 **£9.99**

Richly coloured Merlot-dominated unoaked claret with a likeable leafy-sappy blackcurrant whiff from very ripe fruit all in healthy balance; 14.5% alcohol.

8 Château Maris Les Vieilles Vignes 2016 **£10.99**

Maris is a star property in the Languedoc appellation of Minervois, making lovely big wines from biodynamically cultivated Syrah and Grenache. This one has deep colour and corresponding dark savoury-spicy fruit with its own Mediterranean roasty ripeness; 14% alcohol. Perfect cassoulet red.

9 Georges Duboeuf Chiroubles 2014 **£10.99**

Bumper-scale Beaujolais producer he might be, but Georges Duboeuf, 85, still makes cru wines of spiffing, individual character. This mature Chiroubles is sleek, silky and lush in the best posh-Beaujolais traditions. Duboeuf wines are regularly discounted at Waitrose. I paid £7.99; 13% alcohol. Stop press: 2015 vintage, just tasted, is equally recommended.

RED WINES

FRANCE

8 **Château Saint Sauveur 2012** **£11.39**

Dark, developed Bordeaux 'Supérieur' (fair description in this, but not all, cases) has smoothly convincing ripe black fruits (three years in old oak casks, we gather) just right for accompanying roasted or grilled meats; 13.5% alcohol.

9 **Côtes du Rhône Cairanne Réserve des Hospitaliers 2016** **£11.79**

The new sombre dark label for this hardy perennial might be to camouflage the price hike (way up from the £9.99 for the glorious 2015 vintage) but it's still a bargain in its way, delivering opulent sweetly spicy expensively oak-velveted intense briar-fruit flavours; supple rather than sinewy with a fine trim edge; 14% alcohol.

8 **Les Grands Cèdres Fleurie 2016** **£11.99**

This firmly juicy and really quite grippy Beaujolais classic is potentially delicious, but could do with a year or two to develop in the bottle; 13% alcohol.

10 **Louis Jadot Beaujolais Quincié 2017** **£12.99**

Nick Room, Waitrose's burgundy buyer, worked with Louis Jadot to make this fabulous wine. It's really a Beaujolais Villages as Quincié is not a cru (like Fleurie or Chiroubles) but I believe this is the very best kind of Beaujolais there is: glorious maroon colour, wild (as in riotous) raspberry aromas, and the juiciest, bounciest purple-fruit berry flavours with sensual heft and a fine, crisp acidity to conclude; 12.5% alcohol. Not cheap, but this is Peak Beaujolais!

RED WINES

FRANCE

10 Mischief and Mayhem Bourgogne Pinot Noir 2015 **£14.99**

The name, of course, causes concern, but fear not. This happens to be the generic red burgundy I've liked best all year. Full ruby colour, cool raspberry-strawberry expensive Pinot perfume and evolved earthy-gamey pure Pinot fruit of lovely weight and delicate creaminess; 12% alcohol. It could easily be mistaken (well, I could mistake it, that's for sure) for a very much grander cru burgundy at several times this price.

8 Saint Joseph Cave de Saint-Désirat 2016 **£15.99**

Great but underestimated AC of the northern Rhône makes sleek pure Syrah wines of special savour. Here's a fine introduction: sweetly spicy and silky fruit of long dark savour in fine balance; stands out; 13% alcohol.

8 Château Maris Savoir Vieillir Minervois 2017 **£17.99**

Opaque crimson colour and wild brambly nose are followed up by lush hugely ripe black fruit in a fine silky-spicy (mainly Syrah) rush; 14.5% alcohol. From a biodynamic vineyard within AC Minervois La Livinière this was made without any added sulphur. If it lasts, it might age very gracefully, but it's certainly a treat right now. Exclusive to Waitrose and only 600 cases made, so just in a few stores or online.

RED WINES

FRANCE

8 **Châteauneuf du Pape Le Grand Prébois 2016** **£23.99**

One of a seemingly uncountable number of Châteauneuf wines made by the Perrin family (HQ Ch Beaucastel), this is simply gorgeous, already rounded out and complete with all the complex riches of the famous appellation's best wines; 14.5% alcohol. It's expensive but I'm including it here because Waitrose has offered it at £15.99 during 2018 and might do so again.

GERMANY

9 **Johann Wolf Pinot Noir 2016** **£9.99**

Made by Mosel meister Ernie Loosen, a delightfully bright and crunchy Pinot with raspberry juiciness and plump, silky heft; swish but refreshing to drink cool; 12.5% alcohol.

GREECE

9 **Tsantali Organic Cabernet Sauvignon 2015** **£9.99**

This regular from the coastal resort region of Halkidiki is definitely one to return to year after year. You'll love the bright blackcurrant bloom and the lush, smooth corresponding perky fruit, all brightly trimmed by the clean finish; 13.5% alcohol. You'd never guess it's Greek – or that ancient Greek wine was so ghastly they had to colonise Italy just to plant decent vineyards.

ITALY

8 **Recchia Bardolino 2017** **£7.99**

This cherry bright Veronese aperitif/antipasto red has keen summer red-fruit savour with a white-nut hint cropped by a trim acidity; delightfully fresh and uplifting; 12.5% alcohol.

RED WINES

ITALY

8 Triade 2015 **£8.79**
Generic Puglian from native trio Negroamaro, Primitivo and Nero di Troia delivering deep colour, spiky black-fruit nose and spicy dark heft of ripeness; plumped with oak contact and gently grippy, it's a grand match with meaty pasta sauces; 13.5% alcohol. Often discounted to £6.99 – a snip.

9 Araldica Barbera d'Asti Superiore 2015 **£8.99**
Lovely savoury-pruny and juicy Piedmont stalwart with a bit of richness from oak contact and hallmark blueberry lift to the fruit; generous and intense but perky and juicy besides; 14% alcohol.

8 Tenuta Rapitala Nero d'Avola 2016 **£9.99**
Perkily lush Sicilian indigenous varietal; has the alluring spiciness and sun-baked ripeness that typify many of the island's best wines; 13.5% alcohol.

10 Paolo Leo Primitivo di Manduria 2016 **£10.99**
A night-dark maroon, dense and cushiony pure varietal from Salice Salentino in Puglia that's pitch-perfect at what it does: fascinating plum, morello and cinnamon fruit with a coffee-like roastiness and trim dryness that make it a fine match for pasta as well as charred red meat; 14% alcohol. Reopened next day it actually improves – I know, I am forever buying this on promo at just £7.99.

RED WINES

Waitrose

ITALY

7 Poggio Castagno Chianti Classico 2015 £11.99

I bought this in a moment of madness, lured by a radical price reduction: £11.99 to £7.99. I liked the label's graphic of a Tuscan fattoria amid the vines, and the wine is soft, a little slight, with some sweet Chianti charm; 13% alcohol. But it turns out Poggio Castagno is not a quaint little estate somewhere betwixt Florence and Siena, but a brand name of regional giant Piccini, whose wines throng all the supermarkets in many manifestations. A discount-only deal. Definitely.

8 Waitrose Ripasso di Valpolicella Classico Superiore Fratelli Recchia 2015 £12.99

This dense Veronese speciality is super-ripe rather than raisiny, with deep morello-blackberry fruits and a brisk finish; 14.5% alcohol. Will stand up to spicy menus and strong cheeses.

10 Terre da Vino Barolo 2014 £18.99

It's a peculiarity of Barolo that the intensity of its flavour is rarely matched by that of its colour. Barolo is typically pale, even thin-looking. Not this one. It has the indicative limpid copper hue, but with a fine ruby intensity to it. And the fruit is both piquant and rounded, developing nicely, luscious and long and 13.5% alcohol. Maybe not for purists, but an outstanding example of this great Piedmont name.

9 Terre da Vino Barbaresco Riserva 2010 £18.99

Stablemate to the outstanding Barolo above, this is a hugely enjoyable gamey-ripe and silkily developed classic of impressive maturity at a very fair price; 14% alcohol.

RED WINES

ITALY

8 **Tenuta Tignanello Marchese Antinori Chianti Classico 2014** £29.99

Who knew this is the favourite wine of the Duchess of Sussex, formerly Meghan Markle? Her erstwhile lifestyle blog, The Tig, was named in tribute. It's a jolly good Chianti, vivid and velvety, 13.5% alcohol and fabulously expensive.

NEW ZEALAND

9 **Ara Pinot Noir 2016** £11.99

Agreeable farmyard pong from this ethereally pale Wairau, Marlborough pure varietal, followed up by earthy cherry-strawberry fruit in lush abundance; a revealingly delicious Kiwi Pinot of a memorable kind; 13% alcohol.

PORTUGAL

9 **Gran Passo Classico Lisboa 2016** £7.99

Inky, deep purple wine largely from Port grapes that has the trademark minty-clovey dark-as-night savour to its sweet but grippy black fruit, made enticingly sleek with six months in oak barriques; 14% alcohol. A distinctive bargain.

8 **Ten Mile Bridge 2016** £7.99

Light and well-defined Setubal wine with hallmark Portuguese clove-and-cinnamon spiciness; distinctive match for assertive fish dishes; 13% alcohol. Named in honour of the spectacular Vasco de Gama bridge connecting Lisbon to Setubal.

RED WINES

PORTUGAL

8 **T Trincadeira 2016** **£11.49**

New to me, a fine Alentejo varietal by Aussie David Baverstock, who made his name in Port but has long since moved to the Lisbon region. This grand varietal from indigenous Trincadeira grapes is deep purple and deeply Portuguese with eucalyptus savour to the bold briar fruit and a gentle grip to give a lipsmacking finish; 14.5% alcohol.

SOUTH AFRICA

8 **Swartland Private Collection Pinotage 2017** **£8.29**

Subtle and nuanced by usual Pinotage standards, this yielding pruny-briary oaked spicy-food wine still shows an agreeably characteristic roasty savour; 14% alcohol.

8 **Waitrose Foundation Shiraz 2016** **£8.99**

Barrel-made Cederburg monster red keeps its head of spicy cassis fruit well clear of the oak sheen to make for cleanly edged, stimulating flavours; 14% alcohol.

SPAIN

9 **Waitrose Mellow and Fruity Spanish Red 2017** **£4.99**

Talk of doing what it says on the tin: this is spot-on, a healthy brambly upfront pure Garnacha from Borsao with ripeness (13.5% alcohol) and balance.

8 **Marques de Calatrava Organic Selección Reservada Tempranillo 2017** **£8.79**

New wine to me, from La Mancha, has trademark Tempranillo cassis savour with a certain creaminess (though no oak) and a neat dry edge to the fruit; 13.5% alcohol.

RED WINES

SPAIN

9 San Antolin Reserva Navarra 2010 £9.99

Lively pitch-dark pruny-spicy blackcurranty mature lipsmacker from Rioja's overshadowed neighbour Navarra; largely and most unexpectedly from Merlot and Cabernet Sauvignon topped up with local Graciano grapes; 14% alcohol. Don't be put off by the untrendy label, this is top value, and regularly discounted into the bargain.

9 The Cubist Garnacha 2017 £9.99

An old friend from Calatayud in Zaragoza: formidably dark, dense and ripe, gripping with friendly tannins and full of brambly flavours in a slinky (but unoaked) texture; 14.5% alcohol. Frequently on promo at a bargain £7.99.

PINK WINES

FRANCE

8 Montgravet Cinsault Rosé 2017 £5.99

Shell-pink colour, strawberry scent, matching dry fruit finishing quite dry (well, not quite dry, so to speak), and fresh; 12% alcohol.

8 Le Rosé de Balthazar 2017 £6.99

Pays d'Oc Syrah/Grenache with a delicate hue and bright crispness and freshness finishing properly dry; 12.5% alcohol.

8 Alphonse Mellot Le Paradis Sancerre Rosé 2017 £19.99

If you're a big rosé fan with deep pockets, here's the one, pure Pinot Noir from the Loire's premier appellation Sancerre. Lovely blossom-pink colour, piquant pinot cherry-raspberry nose, delicate but firmly focused corresponding fruit, cool and fresh as the river's own urgent flow, and all that; 13% alcohol.

PINK WINES

NEW ZEALAND

8 **Yealands Sauvignon Blanc Rosé 2017** **£9.99**
How do you make pink wine from green-skinned grapes? Peter Yealands adds 2% Merlot. I liked this because while it looks like rosé (nice colour) it doesn't taste like it. Quite gutsy Kiwi Sauvignon with bright nettly-green-pepper notes and refreshing qualities; 12.5% alcohol.

WHITE WINES

AUSTRALIA

8 **Cumulus Chardonnay 2017** **£9.49**
The naff retro label's a turn-off but this yellow-coloured and big-flavoured Orange, New South Wales pure varietal has a natural ripe stone-fruit flavour and a finely poised fruit-acidity balance that speaks of skilled winemaking; 12.5% alcohol.

9 **Hill-Smith Estate Chardonnay 2017** **£11.99**
Eden Valley (Adelaide) wine is made in what I cannot resist calling the burgundian manner. As such, it's a deliciously plausible creamy and lush dry wine of elegant minerality and poise at price that would seem risible in Beaune; 12.5% alcohol.

AUSTRIA

8 **Waitrose Blueprint Grüner Veltliner 2017** **£8.49**
Dry in the modern manner but with lots of interest from the preserved fruit aromas and a tingle of spiciness; 12.5% alcohol.

9 **Heinrich Hartl Zierfandler 2017** **£14.99**
Entirely new to me, a lemon-gold dry but lush pure varietal that put me in mind of a particularly mineral Chenin Blanc, but with a luscious style all its own and a fine citrus acidity; 12% alcohol. Unhesitatingly commended even at this price.

WHITE WINES

CHILE

8 **Waitrose Blueprint Chilean Sauvignon Blanc 2017** £7.49

Chile makes distinctively gentle and reassuring Sauvignons and here's another one, artfully counterpointing floral aromas and ample white fruits with a keen crisp grassiness and twang of citrus; 13.5% alcohol.

ENGLAND

8 **Waitrose Blueprint English White 2017** £8.99

Good dry Dorking white from Denbies at an almost reasonable price, this has a pleasing colour, interesting white-fruit and brassica nose and grassy fresh savour finishing nice and taut; 12% alcohol. A step in the right direction.

FRANCE

9 **Cuvée Pêcheur 2017** £5.49

I'm giving this serious points because I don't think you can do better for this money. It's from Colombard and Ugni Blanc grown in Gascony, a formula better known for Armagnac than for wine, but it's a masterly dy white, burgeoning with meadow scents and aromatic fruits, tangy and fresh in acidity; 11.5% alcohol.

9 **Le Jardin d'Etoile Sauvignon Blanc 2017** £5.99

'A Loire style Sauvignon', says Waitrose, from a mixture of local and Languedoc grapes. Curious logistics maybe, but this is brilliantly tangy and crisp with a rush of seagrassy fruit and a lemon twist; 12% alcohol. Bargain.

9 **Hauts Les Mains 2017** £6.49

Veritable fruit salad Pays d'Oc with Viognier, Chardonnay and Muscat grapes among others. The mélange is plump with flavours evoking apricot, sweet apple and peach and even grapes, but it's perfectly dry and perfectly delicious into the bargain; 13% alcohol. Aperitif or with salads, natch.

WHITE WINES

FRANCE

Waitrose

9 Voyage au Sud Vermentino 2017 **£6.49**

Vermentino is an Italian grape but here's a Languedoc manifestation, dry but delightfully, herbaceously nuanced with crispness on side with peachy ripeness; 11.5% alcohol. My note says: 'like a much-more-thought-provoking Picpoul de Pinet'. Huh?

8 La Marinière Muscadet 2017 **£6.49**

Heaps of bright white fruit in this briny uncomplicated dry Loire staple and an acidity that's trim rather than eyewatering; 11.5%. Just the thing for moules marinière, obviously.

8 Waitrose Blueprint Sauvignon Blanc 2017 **£7.49**

This Touraine (Loire Valley) wine has a beguiling meadow-grass nose and sunny ripeness of green-fruit flavours; 12% alcohol.

8 Collines de Luzanet Sauvignon Blanc 2017 **£7.99**

Gascon wine (is there anywhere Sauvignon doesn't now grow?) has fine colour, bright gooseberry-green-pepper aromas and fruit all conveyed in a tangy, lemony rush of balanced freshness with modest 11.5% alcohol. It's so clever – more than a match for big Kiwi counterparts.

9 Waitrose Blueprint White Burgundy 2017 **£8.99**

Mâcon Chardonnay of fine gold colour has an enticing sweet-apple Chardonnay perfume with a hint of nectar and a particularly lush but minerally fruit; 13% alcohol. The genuine article, made by a gentleman called Gregoire Pissot.

WHITE WINES

FRANCE

8 Les Andides Chenin Blanc Saumur 2017 £8.99

Bone-dry, river-fresh Loire oyster wine with serious intent; 12.5% alcohol.

8 Les Chartrons Sauvignon Blanc 2017 £9.39

Bordeaux dry Sauvignon has been rather left behind in the rush for its Kiwi counterparts, but this one shows the real distinction: delicate floral-green nose, sunny trace-of-gooseberry fruit, very dry and crisp; 12%. It's uniquely 'elegant' – no kidding.

8 Cave de Beblenheim Kleinfels Riesling 2016 £10.99

Nicely defined Alsace Riesling; big spicy-citrus aroma and full racy-apple fruit with more than a peripheral sweetness, but nevertheless a controlled sweetness. It is, in short, in balance; 13% alcohol. Versatile food white – all the way from smoked salmon to roast duck.

10 Château de Montfort Vouvray 2017 £11.99

World-class wine from a historic Loire estate gorgeously demonstrating the art of balance. The Chenin Blanc in the inadequately named 'demi-sec' style has distant honeysuckle perfume and pebble-fresh brightness of savour; the fruit is exotic, tropical even, but with a perfectly set lime uplift; 12% alcohol. Supreme aperitif white and also a match for lobster, poultry – or pongy cheese.

9 Sancerre Domaine Naudet 2017 £14.99

Domaine Naudet has only about 30 acres of Sauvignon vines, so here's a proper artisan wine, with an almost palpable prickle of freshness in the lavish, leesy, stone-pure Sauvignon fruit; 12.5%. Beautifully balanced and sensibly priced.

WHITE WINES

FRANCE

8 **Château de Cruzeau Blanc 2015** **£17.99**

If you can't live another day without trying a grand chateau-bottled white Graves (Bordeaux), here's the one. It's pure Sauvignon, coloured and perfumed lemon gold and creamy, and dancing with a fruit salad of lush green flavours; 13.5% alcohol. Price looks a snip compared to grandest Graves estates at £300-plus.

8 **St Aubin Premier Cru Domaine Gérard Thomas 2016** **£24.99**

Neighbouring Chassagne-Montrachet in Burgundy's heartland, St Aubin is a quietly brilliant source of serious Chardonnays. This luscious and leesy dry wine has fine white- and stone-fruit ripeness, stranded with discreetly creamy oak; 13% alcohol. A safe bet for a special occasion.

GERMANY

8 **Vom Löss Pinot Blanc 2016** **£7.99**

Yet another German Pinot Blanc, this time from the Rheinpfalz and with smoky green fruit and white nut style in the Alsace manner, trimmed with a distinct grapefruit twang; keen, refreshing and interesting; 12.5% alcohol.

9 **Dr Loosen Urziger Würzgarten Riesling Kabinett 2016** **£15.99**

Piercingly pure moselle, delicately weighted but metaphorically viscous in its concentration of racy, mineral Riesling fruit; 8% alcohol. I occasionally take this wine to Schloss von Bülow, where it is warmly appreciated.

ITALY

8 **Corbello Catarratto/Chardonnay 2017** **£7.99**

Tangy opening flavour morphs into peachy-melon in this intriguing and likeable Sicilian just-dry white; 12% alcohol. Creamy pasta as well as every description of fish.

WHITE WINES

ITALY

8 Pecorino Terre di Chieti 2017 £7.99
Endearing sheep graphic on this bright Abruzzo dry white references the constituent grape Pecorino, supposedly named from Italian *pecaro* for sheep because the variety flourishes on grazing land. Actually the wine does have a grassy lushness as well as a likeable grapefruit twang; 12% alcohol.

8 Maree d'Ione Organic Fiano 2017 £8.79
Puglian dry wine has the authentic wild herby, bee-luring blossomy apple-and-pear fruit of the Fiano niftily counterpointed by lime and grapefruit acidity in fine harmony; 12.5% alcohol.

9 La Vis Storie di Vite Pinot Grigio 2017 £9.99
From the foothills of the Dolomites, this is frequently my favourite supermarket PG because it conveys the character of the grape: smoky, spicy, stony-fresh and bright with crisp fruit; 12% alcohol.

8 Gavi del Commune di Capriato d'Orba Venturina 2017 £10.79
Gavi is everywhere. This is in the fuller, nuttier style but still with a good whoosh of sleek green fruits and limey acidity; 12% alcohol.

9 Tre Fiori Greco di Tufo 2017 £10.99
Lush, lemony food-matching dry wine from the Campania is affectingly bright and fresh with ripe, melon-mango undercurrent of flavours; really quite special; 12.5% alcohol.

WHITE WINES

ITALY

8 Zenato Villa Flora Lugana 2017 **£10.99**

Stylish Venetian wine, dry but long and slaking with a bit of crafty sweet nuttiness amid the elegant green-gold fruit; 12% alcohol. Distinctive.

NEW ZEALAND

8 Cowrie Bay Sauvignon Blanc 2017 **£7.49**

Taut Marlborough wine delivering asparagus, nettle and ripe but brisk authentic fruit at a sensible price; 12.5% alcohol.

8 Peter Yealands Reserve Sauvignon Blanc 2017 **£11.59**

Yealands deserves his renown, won for wines like this shimmering fully ripe grassy pure varietal with an appreciable heft of fruit and snappy acidity. The quality is very clear and warrants the price.

SOUTH AFRICA

9 The Search Grenache Blanc/Marsanne/Roussanne 2017 **£9.99**

Complex lavish blend in the style of succulent Rhône whites, unoaked but leesy; uplifting in its acidity and entirely convincing; 13% alcohol. A fine piece of work from the Cape's emerging Voor Paardeberg region at a good price.

8 Dawn Patrol Sauvignon Blanc 2017 **£9.99**

Tangy, even bracing, Sauvignon-Semillon blend with a contrasting rich centre of green-gold ripeness en route to the keen citrus edge; a fascinator, at once refreshing and intriguing; 13% alcohol.

WHITE WINES

SOUTH AFRICA

9 **Kaapzicht Kliprug Bush Vine Chenin Blanc 2017** **£13.99**

The Afrikaans name Kaapzicht Kliprug might roll a bit rocky off the tongue but this gorgeous tropical-fruit dry wine is a snip to sip. The gold colour and guava-honeydew aromas and flavours are almost Sauternes-like in their ambrosial evocations and yet this really is a dry wine, lifted by apple-crisp notes and a textbook citrus acidity; 13.5% alcohol.

SPAIN

8 **Baron de Ley Rioja Blanco 2017** **£8.99**

Modern unoaked, unoxidised style (long since extinct I'm sad to believe) this is still a fleshy, leesy even lush dry wine nevertheless; 13% alcohol. Good paella white.

8 **Tres Mares Albariño 2017** **£9.99**

Rias Baixas wine has good colour, tangy seagrass aroma and bracing brassica-citrus green flavours with plenty of generous fruit; 12.5% alcohol; stands out from a burgeoning crowd.

SPARKLING WINES

ARGENTINA

7 **Chandon Brut** **£16.99**

Champagne-formula fizz from Mendoza with a mildly burnt-toast aroma and savour which intrigues, and lots of familiar fruit flavours; 12.5% alcohol.

SPARKLING WINES

ENGLAND

8 **Leckford Estate Brut 2013** **£26.99**

Hampshire sparkler from the champagne varieties proceeds from a lemony top note into fine ripe fruits and a stimulating finish; 12% alcohol. It's not like champagne, but it's thoroughly likeable in its own way.

9 **Nyetimber Classic Cuvée** **£34.99**

Pioneering Sussex winery benefitting from its relatively long history, with Chardonnay and Pinots Noir and Meunier vines now 30 years old. I believe this is like good champagne, mellow in colour, warm-bakery aromas and flavours with a persistent tiny-bubble mousse; 12% alcohol. Yes it's expensive (though Waitrose have offered it on promo for £25.99 in 2018) but it's a class product.

FRANCE

8 **Prince Alexandre Crémant de Loire Brut** **£12.99**

Very dry apple-crisp and likeable leesy-yeasty eager fizz from Chenin Blanc with added Chardonnay and Cabernet Franc. Commands attention and tastes convincing; 13% alcohol.

9 **Waitrose Blanc de Noirs Champagne Brut** **£22.99**

Saucy lick of luscious ripeness in this bright and stimulating pure Pinot Noir, which Waitrose helpfully points out includes reserve wines from vintages dating back to 2009; 12% alcohol.

SPARKLING WINES

FRANCE

8 **Waitrose Blanc de Blancs Champagne Brut** **£23.99**

This dependable perennial has a rather chilly-looking new blue label which I did not warm to. Still the same eager all-Chardonnay bright and nuanced bready refresher though; 12.5% alcohol.

ITALY

8 **Casuzze Organic Grillo Spumante Brut** **£11.99**

It's Italian and it's not Prosecco – give it a try. Admirable Grillo grapes organically grown in Sicily make this dry, crisp, lemony, apple-pear fruit foaming refresher at 12.5% alcohol.

Enjoying it

Drink or keep?

Wines from supermarkets should be ready to drink as soon as you get them home. Expensive reds of recent vintage, for example from Bordeaux or the Rhône, sold as seasonal specials, might benefit from a few years' 'cellaring'. If in doubt, look up your purchase on a web vintage chart to check.

Some wines certainly need drinking sooner than others. Dry whites and rosés won't improve with time. Good-quality red wines will happily endure, even improve, for years if they're kept at a constant moderate temperature, preferably away from bright light, and on their sides so corks don't dry out. Supermarkets like to advise us on back labels of red wines to consume the product within a year or two. Pay no attention.

Champagne, including supermarket own-label brands, almost invariably improves with keeping. Evolving at rest is what champagne is all about. Continue the process at home. I like to wait for price promotions, buy in bulk and hoard the booty in smug certainty of a bargain that's also an improving asset. None of this applies to any other kind of sparkling wine – especially prosecco.

Of more immediate urgency is the matter of keeping wine in good condition once you've opened it. Recorked leftovers should last a day, but after that the wine will oxidise, turning stale and sour. There is a variety of wine-saving stopper devices, but I have yet to find one that works. My preferred method is to decant leftovers into a smaller bottle with a pull-cork or screwcap. Top it right up.

Early opening

Is there any point in uncorking a wine in advance to allow it to 'breathe'? Absolutely none. The stale air trapped between the top of the wine and the bottom of the cork (or screwcap) disperses at once and the 1cm circle of liquid exposed will have a negligible response to the atmosphere. Decanting the wine will certainly make a difference, but whether it's a beneficial difference is a matter for conjecture – unless you're decanting to get the wine off its lees or sediment.

Beware trying to warm up an icy bottle of red. If you put it close to a heat source, take the cork out first. As the wine warms, even mildly, it gives off gas that will spoil the flavour if it cannot escape.

Chill factor

White wine, rosé and sparkling wines all need to be cold. It's the law. The degree of chill is a personal choice but icy temperatures can mask the flavours of good wines. Bad wines, on the other hand, might benefit from overchilling. The anaesthetic effect removes the sense of taste.

Red wines can respond well to mild chilling. Beaujolais and stalky reds of the Loire such as Chinon and Saumur are brighter when cool, as is Bardolino from Verona and lighter Pinot Noir from everywhere.

Is it off?

Once there was a plague of 'corked' wine. It's over. Wine bottlers have eliminated most of the causes. Principal among them was TCA or trichloroanisole 123, an infection of the raw material from which corks are made, namely the bark of cork oak trees. New technology developed by firms such as Portuguese cork giant Amorim has finally made all cork taint-free.

TCA spawned an alternative-closure industry that has prospered mightily through the supply of polymer stoppers and screwcaps. The polymer products, although unnecessary now that corks are so reliable, persist. They're pointless: awkward to extract and to reinsert, and allegedly less environmentally friendly than natural corks.

Screwcaps persist too, but they have their merits. They obviate the corkscrew and can be replaced on the bottle. They are recyclable. Keep them on the bottles you take to the bottle bank.

Some closures will, of course, occasionally fail due to material faults or malfunctions in bottling that allow air into the bottle. The dull, sour effects on wine of oxidation are obvious, and you should return any offending bottle to the supplier for a replacement or refund. Supermarkets in my experience are pretty good about this.

Wines that are bad because they are poorly made are a bit more complicated. You might just hate it because it's not to your taste – too sweet or too dry, too dense or too light – in which case, bad luck. But if it has classic (though now rare) faults such as mustiness, a vinegar taint (volatile acidity or acetate), cloudiness or a suspension of particles, don't drink it. Recork it and take it back to the supplier.

Glass action

There is something like a consensus in the wine world about the right kind of drinking glass. It should consist of a clear, tulip-shaped bowl on a comfortably long stem. You hold the glass by the stem so you can admire the colour of the wine and keep the bowl free of fingermarks. The bowl is big enough to hold a sensible quantity of wine at about half full. Good wine glasses have a fine bevelled surface at the rim of the bowl. Cheap glasses have a rolled rim that catches your lip and, I believe, materially diminishes the enjoyment of the wine.

Good wine glasses deserve care. Don't put them in the dishwasher. Over time, they'll craze. To maintain the crystal clarity of glasses wash them in hot soapy water, rinse clean with hot water and dry immediately with a glass cloth kept exclusively for this purpose. Sounds a bit nerdy maybe, but it can make all the difference.

What to eat with it?

When tasting a hundred or more wines one after the other and trying to make lucid notes on each of them, the mind can crave diversion. Besides describing the appearance, aroma and taste, as I'm supposed to do, I often muse on what sort of food the wine might suit.

Some of these whimsical observations make it into the finished reports for this book. Like all the rest of it, they are my own subjective opinion, but maybe they help set the wines in some sort of context.

Conventions such as white wine with fish and red with meat might be antiquated, but they can still inhibit choice. If you only like white wine must you abstain on carnivorous occasions – or go veggie? Obviously not. Much better to give detailed thought to the possibilities, and go in for plenty of experimentation.

Ripe whites from grapes such as Chardonnay can match all white meats, cured meats and barbecued meats, and most saucy meat dishes too. With bloody chunks of red meat, exotic whites from the Rhône Valley or Alsace or oaky Rioja Blanco all come immediately to mind.

As for those who prefer red wine at all times, there are few fish dishes that spurn everything red. Maybe a crab salad or a grilled Dover sole. But as soon as you add sauce, red's back on the menu. Again, the answer is to experiment.

Some foods do present particular difficulties. Nibbles such as salty peanuts or vinegary olives will clash with most table wines. So buy some proper dry sherry, chill it down and thrill to the world's best aperitif. Fino, manzanilla and amontillado sherries of real quality now feature in all the best supermarkets – some under own labels.

Eggs are supposed to be inimical to wine. Boiled, fried or poached certainly. But an omelette with a glass of wine, of any colour, is surely a match. Salads, especially those with fruit or tomatoes, get the thumbs-down, but I think it's the dressing. Forgo the vinegar, and salad opens up a vinous vista.

Cheese is a conundrum. Red wine goes with cheese, right? But soft cheeses, particularly goat's, can make red wines taste awfully tinny. You're much better off with an exotic and ripe white wine. Sweet white wines make a famously savoury match with blue cheeses. A better match, I believe, than with their conventional companions, puddings. Hard cheeses such as Cheddar may be fine with some red wines, but even better with a glass of Port.

Wine with curry? Now that incendiary dishes are entirely integrated into the national diet, I suppose this is, uh, a burning question. Big, ripe reds such as Australian Shiraz can stand up to Indian heat, and Argentine Malbec seems appropriate for chilli dishes. Chinese cuisine likes aromatic white wines such as Alsace (or New Zealand) Gewürztraminer, and salsa dishes call for zingy dry whites such as Sauvignon Blanc.

But everyone to their own taste. If there's one universal convention in food and wine matching it must surely be to suit yourself.

A Wine Vocabulary

A brief guide to the use of language across the wine world – on labels, in literature and among the listings in this book

A

AC – *See* Appellation d'Origine Contrôlée.

acidity – Natural acids in grape juice are harnessed by the winemaker to produce clean, crisp flavours. Excess acidity creates rawness or greenness; shortage is indicated by wateriness.

aftertaste – The flavour that lingers in the mouth after swallowing or spitting the wine.

Aglianico – Black grape variety of southern Italy. Vines originally planted by ancient Greek settlers from 600BC in the arid volcanic landscapes of Basilicata and Cilento produce distinctive dark and earthy reds.

Agriculture biologique – On French wine labels, an indication that the wine has been made by organic methods.

Albariño – White grape variety of Spain that makes intriguingly perfumed fresh and tangy dry wines, especially in esteemed Atlantic-facing Rias Baixas region.

alcohol – The alcohol levels in wines are expressed in terms of alcohol by volume ('abv'), that is, the percentage of the volume of the wine that is common, or ethyl, alcohol. A typical wine at 12 per cent abv is thus 12 parts alcohol and, in effect, 88 parts fruit juice. Alcohol is viewed by some health professionals as a poison, but there is actuarial evidence that total abstainers live shorter lives than moderate consumers. The UK Department of Health declares there is no safe level of alcohol consumption, and advises that drinkers should not exceed a weekly number of 'units' of alcohol. A unit is 10ml of pure alcohol, the quantity contained in about half a 175ml glass of wine with 12 per cent alcohol. From 1995, the advisory limit on weekly units was 28 for men and 21 for women. This was reduced in 2016 to 14 for men and women alike.

Alentejo – Wine region of southern Portugal (immediately north of the Algarve), with a fast-improving reputation, especially for sappy, keen reds from local grape varieties including Aragones, Castelão and Trincadeira.

Almansa – DO winemaking region of Spain inland from Alicante, making inexpensive red wines.

Alsace – France's easternmost wine-producing region lies between the Vosges Mountains and the River Rhine, with Germany beyond.

These conditions make for the production of some of the world's most delicious and fascinating white wines, always sold under the name of their constituent grapes. Pinot Blanc is the most affordable – and is well worth looking out for. The 'noble' grape varieties of the region are Gewürztraminer, Muscat, Riesling and Pinot Gris and they are always made on a single-variety basis. The richest, most exotic wines are those from individual *grand cru* vineyards, which are named on the label. Some *vendange tardive* (late harvest) wines are made, and tend to be expensive. All the wines are sold in tall, slim green bottles known as flûtes that closely resemble those of the Mosel. The names of producers as well as grape varieties are often German too, so it is widely assumed that Alsace wines are German in style, if not in nationality. But this is not the case in either particular. Alsace wines are dry and quite unique in character – and definitely French.

amarone – Style of red wine made in Valpolicella, Italy. Specially selected grapes are held back from the harvest and stored for several months to dry them out. They are then pressed and fermented into a highly concentrated speciality dry wine. Amarone means 'bitter', describing the dry style of the flavour.

amontillado – *See* sherry.

aperitif – If a wine is thus described, I believe it will give as much pleasure before a meal as with one. Crisp, low-alcohol German wines and other delicately flavoured whites (including many dry Italians) are examples.

appassimento – Italian technique of drying out new-picked grapes to concentrate the sugars. Varying proportions of appassimento fruit are added to the fermentation of speciality wines such as amarone and ripasso.

Appellation d'Origine Contrôlée – Commonly abbreviated to AC or AOC, this is the system under which top-quality wines have been defined in France since 1935. About a third of the country's vast annual output qualifies across about 500 AC (or AOP - see Appellation d'Origine Protégée) zones. The declaration of an AC on the label signifies that the wine meets standards concerning location of vineyards and wineries, grape varieties and limits on harvest per hectare, methods of cultivation and vinification, and alcohol content. Wines are inspected and tasted by state-appointed committees.

Appellation d'Origine Protégée (AOP) – Under European Union rule changes, the AOC system is gradually transforming into AOP. In effect, it means little more than the exchange of 'controlled' with 'protected' on labels. One quirk of the rules is that makers of AOP wines will be able to name the constituent grape variety or varieties on their labels, if they so wish.

Apulia – Anglicised name for Puglia, Italy.

Aragones – Synonym in Portugal, especially in the Alentejo region, for the Tempranillo grape variety of Spain.

Ardèche – Region of southern France to the west of the Rhône river, home to a good IGP zone including the Coteaux de l'Ardèche. Decent-value reds from Syrah and Cabernet Sauvignon grapes, and less interesting dry whites.

Arneis – White grape variety of Piedmont, north-west Italy. Makes dry whites with a certain almondy richness at often-inflated prices.

Assyrtiko – White grape variety of Greece now commonly named on dry white wines, sometimes of great quality, from the mainland and islands.

Asti – Town and major winemaking centre in Piedmont, Italy. The sparkling (spumante) wines made from Moscato grapes are inexpensive and sweet with a modest 5 to 7 per cent alcohol. Vivid red wine Barbera d'Asti also produced.

attack – In wine-tasting, the first impression made by the wine in the mouth.

Auslese – German wine-quality designation. *See* QmP.

B

Baga – Black grape variety indigenous to Portugal. Makes famously concentrated, juicy reds of deep colour from the grapes' particularly thick skins. Look out for this name, now quite frequently quoted as the varietal on Portuguese wine labels.

balance – A big word in the vocabulary of wine tasting. Respectable wine must get two key things right: lots of fruitiness from the sweet grape juice, and plenty of acidity so the sweetness is 'balanced' with the crispness familiar in good dry whites and the dryness that marks out good reds. Some wines are noticeably 'well balanced' in that they have memorable fruitiness and the clean, satisfying 'finish' (last flavour in the mouth) that ideal acidity imparts.

Barbera – Black grape variety originally of Piedmont in Italy. Most commonly seen as Barbera d'Asti, the vigorously fruity red wine made around Asti – once better known for sweet sparkling Asti Spumante. Barbera grapes are now cultivated in South America, producing less-interesting wine than at home in Italy.

Bardolino – Once fashionable, light red wine DOC of Veneto, north-west Italy. Bardolino is made principally from Corvina Veronese grapes plus Rondinella, Molinara and Negrara. Best wines are supposed to be those labelled Bardolino Superiore, a DOCG created in 2002. This classification closely specifies the permissible grape varieties and sets the alcohol level at a minimum of 12 per cent.

Barossa Valley – Famed vineyard region north of Adelaide, Australia, produces hearty reds principally from Shiraz, Cabernet Sauvignon and Grenache grapes, plus plenty of lush white wine from Chardonnay. Also known for limey, long-lived, mineral dry whites from Riesling grapes.

barrique – Barrel in French. *En barrique* on a wine label signifies the wine has been matured in casks rather than tanks.

Beaujolais – Unique red wines from the southern reaches of Burgundy, France, are made from Gamay grapes. Beaujolais nouveau, now unfashionable, provides a friendly introduction to the bouncy, red-fruit style of the wine, but for the authentic experience, go for Beaujolais Villages, from the region's better, northern vineyards. There are ten AC zones within this northern sector making wines under their own names. Known as the *crus*, these are Brouilly, Chénas, Chiroubles, Côte de Brouilly,

Fleurie, Juliénas, Morgon, Moulin à Vent, Regnié and St Amour. Prices are higher than those for Beaujolais Villages, but not always justifiably so.

Beaumes de Venise – Village near Châteauneuf du Pape in France's Rhône valley, famous for sweet and alcoholic wine from Muscat grapes. Delicious, grapey wines. A small number of growers also make strong (sometimes rather tough) red wines under the village name.

Beaune – One of the two centres (the other is Nuits St Georges) of the Côte d'Or, the winemaking heart of Burgundy in France. Three of the region's humbler appellations take the name of the town: Côtes de Beaune, Côtes de Beaune Villages and Hautes Côtes de Beaune.

berry fruit – Some red wines deliver a burst of flavour in the mouth that corresponds to biting into a newly picked berry – strawberry, blackberry, etc. So a wine described as having berry fruit (by this writer, anyway) has freshness, liveliness and immediate appeal.

bianco – White wine, Italy.

Bical – White grape variety principally of Dão region of northern Portugal. Not usually identified on labels, because most of it goes into inexpensive sparkling wines. Can make still wines of very refreshing crispness.

biodynamics – A cultivation method taking the organic approach several steps further. Biodynamic winemakers plant and tend their vineyards according to a date and time calendar 'in harmony' with the movements of the planets. Some of France's best-known wine estates subscribe, and many more are going that way. It might all sound bonkers, but it's salutary to learn that biodynamics is based on principles first described by the eminent Austrian educationist Rudolph Steiner.

bite – In wine-tasting, the impression on the palate of a wine with plenty of acidity and, often, tannin.

blanc – White wine, France.

blanc de blancs – White wine from white grapes, France. May seem to be stating the obvious, but some white wines (e.g. champagne) are made, partially or entirely, from black grapes.

blanc de noirs – White wine from black grapes, France. Usually sparkling (especially champagne) made from black Pinot Meunier and Pinot Noir grapes, with no Chardonnay or other white varieties.

blanco – White wine, Spain and Portugal.

Blauer Zweigelt – Black grape variety of Austria, making a large proportion of the country's red wines, some of excellent quality.

Bobal – Black grape variety mostly of south-eastern Spain. Thick skin is good for colour and juice contributes acidity to blends.

bodega – In Spain, a wine producer or wine shop.

Bonarda – Black grape variety of northern Italy. Now more widely planted in Argentina, where it makes some well-regarded red wines.

botrytis – Full name, *botrytis cinerea*, is that of a beneficent fungus that can attack ripe grape bunches late in the season, shrivelling the berries to a gruesome-looking mess, which yields concentrated juice of prized sweetness. Cheerfully known as 'noble rot', this fungus is actively encouraged by winemakers in regions as diverse as Sauternes (in Bordeaux),

Monbazillac (in Bergerac), the Rhine and Mosel valleys, Hungary's Tokaji region and South Australia to make ambrosial dessert wines.

bouncy – The feel in the mouth of a red wine with young, juicy fruitiness. Good Beaujolais is bouncy, as are many north-west-Italian wines from Barbera and Dolcetto grapes.

Bourgogne Grand Ordinaire – Former AC of Burgundy, France. *See* Coteaux Bourguignons.

Bourgueil – Appellation of Loire Valley, France. Long-lived red wines from Cabernet Franc grapes.

briary – In wine tasting, associated with the flavours of fruit from prickly bushes such as blackberries.

brûlé – Pleasant burnt-toffee taste or smell, as in crème brûlée.

brut – Driest style of sparkling wine. Originally French, for very dry champagnes specially developed for the British market, but now used for sparkling wines from all round the world.

Buzet – Little-seen AC of south-west France overshadowed by Bordeaux but producing some characterful ripe reds.

C

Cabardès – AC for red and rosé wines from area north of Carcassonne, Aude, France. Principally Cabernet Sauvignon and Merlot grapes.

Cabernet Franc – Black grape variety originally of France. It makes the light-bodied and keenly edged red wines of the Loire Valley – such as Chinon and Saumur. And it is much grown in Bordeaux, especially in the appellation of St Emilion. Also now planted in Argentina, Australia and North America. Wines, especially in the Loire, are characterised by a leafy, sappy style and bold fruitiness. Most are best enjoyed young.

Cabernet Sauvignon – Black (or, rather, blue) grape variety now grown in virtually every wine-producing nation. When perfectly ripened, the grapes are smaller than many other varieties and have particularly thick skins. This means that when pressed, Cabernet grapes have a high proportion of skin to juice – and that makes for wine with lots of colour and tannin. In Bordeaux, the grape's traditional home, the grandest Cabernet-based wines have always been known as *vins de garde* (wines to keep) because they take years, even decades, to evolve as the effect of all that skin extraction preserves the fruit all the way to magnificent maturity. But in today's impatient world, these grapes are exploited in modern winemaking techniques to produce the sublime flavours of mature Cabernet without having to hang around for lengthy periods awaiting maturation. While there's nothing like a fine, ten-year-old claret (and few quite as expensive), there are many excellent Cabernets from around the world that amply illustrate this grape's characteristics. Classic smells and flavours include blackcurrants, cedar wood, chocolate, tobacco – even violets.

Cahors – An AC of the Lot Valley in south-west France once famous for 'black wine'. This was a curious concoction of straightforward wine mixed with a soupy must, made by boiling up new-pressed juice to concentrate it (through evaporation) before fermentation. The myth is still perpetuated that Cahors wine continues to be made in this way, but production on this basis actually ceased 150 years ago. Cahors today is no stronger, or blacker, than the wines of neighbouring appellations. Principal grape variety is Malbec, known locally as Cot.

Cairanne – Village of the appellation collectively known as the Côtes du Rhône in southern France. Cairanne is one of several villages entitled to put their name on the labels of wines made within their AC boundary, and the appearance of this name is quite reliably an indicator of quality.

Calatayud – DO (quality wine zone) near Zaragoza in the Aragon region of northern Spain where they're making some astonishingly good wines at bargain prices, mainly reds from Garnacha and Tempranillo grapes. These are the varieties that go into the polished and oaky wines of Rioja, but in Calatayud, the wines are dark, dense and decidedly different.

Cannonau – Black grape native to Sardinia by name, but in fact the same variety as the ubiquitous Grenache of France (and Garnacha of Spain).

cantina sociale – *See* co-op.

Carignan – Black grape variety of Mediterranean France. It is rarely identified on labels, but is a major constituent of wines from the southern Rhône and Languedoc-Roussillon regions. Known as Carignano in Italy and Cariñena in Spain.

Cariñena – A region of north-east Spain, south of Navarra, known for substantial reds, as well as the Spanish name for the Carignan grape (*qv*).

Carmenère – Black grape variety once widely grown in Bordeaux but abandoned due to cultivation problems. Lately revived in South America where it is producing fine wines, sometimes with echoes of Bordeaux.

cassis – As a tasting note, signifies a wine that has a noticeable blackcurrant-concentrate flavour or smell. Much associated with the Cabernet Sauvignon grape.

Castelao – Portuguese black grape variety. Same as Periquita.

Catarratto – White grape variety of Sicily. In skilled hands it can make anything from keen, green-fruit dry whites to lush, oaked super-ripe styles. Also used for Marsala.

cat's pee – In tasting notes, a jocular reference to the smell of a certain style of Sauvignon Blanc wine.

cava – The sparkling wine of Spain. Most originates in Catalonia, but the Denominación de Origen (DO) guarantee of authenticity is open to producers in many regions of the country. Much cava is very reasonably priced even though it is made by the same method as champagne – second fermentation in bottle, known in Spain as the *método clásico*.

CdR – Côtes du Rhône. My own shorthand.

cépage – Grape variety, French. 'Cépage Merlot' on a label simply means the wine is made largely or exclusively from Merlot grapes.

Chablis – Northernmost AC of France's Burgundy region. Its dry white wines from Chardonnay grapes are known for their fresh and steely style, but the best wines also age very gracefully into complex classics.

Chambourcin – Sounds like a cream cheese but it's a relatively modern (1963) French hybrid black grape that makes some good non-appellation lightweight-but-concentrated reds in the Loire Valley and now some heftier versions in Australia.

champagne – The sparkling wine of the strictly defined Champagne region of France, made by the equally strictly defined champagne method.

Chardonnay – Possibly the world's most popular grape variety. Said to originate from the village of Chardonnay in the Mâconnais region of southern Burgundy, the vine is now planted in every wine-producing nation. Wines are commonly characterised by generous colour and sweet-apple smell, but styles range from lean and sharp to opulently rich. Australia started the craze for oaked Chardonnay, the gold-coloured, super-ripe, buttery 'upfront' wines that are a caricature of lavish and outrageously expensive burgundies such as Meursault and Puligny-Montrachet. Rich to the point of egginess, these Aussie pretenders are now giving way to a sleeker, more minerally style with much less oak presence – if any at all. California and Chile, New Zealand and South Africa are competing hard to imitate the Burgundian style, and Australia's success in doing so.

Châteauneuf du Pape – Famed appellation centred on a picturesque village of the southern Rhône valley in France where in the 1320s French Pope Clement V had a splendid new château built for himself as a summer retreat amidst his vineyards. The red wines of the AC, which can be made from 13 different grape varieties but principally Grenache, Syrah and Mourvèdre, are regarded as the best of the southern Rhône and have become rather expensive – but they can be sensationally good. Expensive white wines are also made.

Chenin Blanc – White grape variety of the Loire Valley, France. Now also grown farther afield, especially in South Africa. Makes dry, soft white wines and also rich, sweet styles.

cherry – In wine tasting, either a pale red colour or, more commonly, a smell or flavour akin to the sun-warmed, bursting sweet ripeness of cherries. Many Italian wines, from lightweights such as Bardolino and Valpolicella to serious Chianti, have this character. 'Black cherry' as a description is often used of Merlot wines – meaning they are sweet but have a firmness of mouthfeel associated with the thicker skins of black cherries.

Cinsault – Black grape variety of southern France, where it is invariably blended with others in wines of all qualities from country reds to pricy appellations such as Châteauneuf du Pape. Also much planted in South Africa. The effect in wine is to add keen aromas (sometimes compared with turpentine) and softness to the blend. The name is often spelt Cinsaut.

Clape, La – A small *cru* (defined quality-vineyard area) within the Coteaux du Languedoc where the growers make some seriously delicious red wines, mainly from Carignan, Grenache and Syrah grapes. A name worth looking out for on labels from the region.

claret – The red wine of Bordeaux, France. Old British nickname from Latin *clarus*, meaning 'clear', recalling a time when the red wines of the region were much lighter in colour than they are now.

clarete – On Spanish labels indicates a pale-coloured red wine. Tinto signifies a deeper hue.

classed growth – English translation of French *cru classé* describes a group of 60 individual wine estates in the Médoc district of Bordeaux, which in 1855 were granted this new status on the basis that their wines were the most expensive of the day. The classification was a promotional wheeze to attract attention to the Bordeaux stand at that year's Great Exhibition in Paris. Amazingly, all of the wines concerned are still in production and most still occupy more or less their original places in the pecking order price-wise. The league was divided up into five divisions from *Premier Grand Cru Classé* (just four wines originally, with one promoted in 1971 – the only change ever made to the classification) to *Cinquième Grand Cru Classé*. Other regions of Bordeaux, notably Graves and St Emilion, have since imitated Médoc and introduced their own rankings of *cru classé* estates.

classic – An overused term in every respect – wine descriptions being no exception. In this book, the word is used to describe a very good wine of its type. So, a 'classic' Cabernet Sauvignon is one that is recognisably and admirably characteristic of that grape.

Classico – Under Italy's wine laws, this word appended to the name of a DOC or DOCG zone has an important significance. The classico wines of the region can only be made from vineyards lying in the best-rated areas, and wines thus labelled (e.g. Chianti Classico, Soave Classico, Valpolicella Classico) can be reliably counted on to be a cut above the rest.

Colombard – White grape variety of southern France. Once employed almost entirely for making the wine that is distilled for armagnac and cognac brandies, but lately restored to varietal prominence in the Côtes de Gascogne where high-tech wineries turn it into a fresh and crisp, if unchallenging, dry wine at a budget price. But beware, cheap Colombard (especially from South Africa) can still be very dull.

Conca de Barbera – Winemaking region of Catalonia, Spain.

co-op – Very many of France's good-quality, inexpensive wines are made by co-operatives. These are wine-producing centres whose members, and joint-owners, are local *vignerons* (vine growers). Each year they sell their harvests to the co-op for turning into branded wines. In Italy, co-op wines can be identified by the words *Cantina Sociale* on the label and in Germany by the term *Winzergenossenschaft*.

Corbières – A name to look out for. It's an AC of France's Midi (deep south) and produces countless robust reds and a few interesting whites, often at bargain prices.

Cortese – White grape variety of Piedmont, Italy. At its best, makes delicious, keenly brisk and fascinating wines, including those of the Gavi DOCG. Worth seeking out.

Costières de Nîmes – Until 1989, this AC of southern France was known as the Costières de Gard. It forms a buffer between the southern Rhône and Languedoc-Roussillon regions, and makes wines from broadly the same range of grape varieties. It's a name to look out for, the best red wines being notable for their concentration of colour and fruit, with the earthy-spiciness of the better Rhône wines and a likeable liquorice note. A few good white wines, too, and even a decent rosé or two.

Côte – In French, it simply means a side, or slope, of a hill. The implication in wine terms is that the grapes come from a vineyard ideally situated for maximum sunlight, good drainage and the unique soil conditions prevailing on the hill in question. It's fair enough to claim that vines grown on slopes might get more sunlight than those grown on the flat, but there is no guarantee whatsoever that any wine labelled 'Côtes du' this or that is made from grapes grown on a hillside anyway. Côtes du Rhône wines are a case in point. Many 'Côtes' wines come from entirely level vineyards and it is worth remembering that many of the vineyards of Bordeaux, producing most of the world's priciest wines, are little short of prairie-flat. The quality factor is determined much more significantly by the weather and the talents of the winemaker.

Coteaux Bourguignons – Generic AC of Burgundy, France, since 2011 for red and rosé wines from Pinot Noir and Gamay grapes, and white wines from (principally) Chardonnay and Bourgogne Aligoté grapes. The AC replaces the former appellation Bourgogne Grand Ordinaire.

Côtes de Blaye – Appellation Contrôlée zone of Bordeaux on the right bank of the River Gironde, opposite the more prestigious Médoc zone of the left bank. Best-rated vineyards qualify for the AC Premières Côtes de Blaye. A couple of centuries ago, Blaye (pronounced 'bligh') was the grander of the two, and even today makes some wines that compete well for quality, and at a fraction of the price of wines from its more fashionable rival across the water.

Côtes de Bourg – AC neighbouring Côtes de Blaye, making red wines of decent quality and value.

Côtes du Luberon – Appellation Contrôlée zone of Provence in south-east France. Wines, mostly red, are similar in style to Côtes du Rhône.

Côtes du Rhône – One of the biggest and best-known appellations of south-east France, covering an area roughly defined by the southern reaches of the valley of the River Rhône. The Côtes du Rhône AC achieves notably consistent quality at all points along the price scale. Lots of brilliant-value warm and spicy reds, principally from Grenache and Syrah grapes. There are also some white and rosé wines.

Côtes du Rhône Villages – Appellation within the larger Côtes du Rhône AC for wine of supposed superiority made in a number of zones associated with a long list of nominated individual villages.

Côtes du Roussillon – Huge appellation of south-west France known for strong, dark, peppery reds often offering very decent value.

Côtes du Roussillon Villages – Appellation for superior wines from a number of nominated locations within the larger Roussillon AC. Some of these village wines can be of exceptional quality and value.

crianza – Means 'nursery' in Spanish. On Rioja and Navarra wines, the designation signifies a wine that has been nursed through a maturing period of at least a year in oak casks and a further six months in bottle before being released for sale.

cru – A word that crops up with confusing regularity on French wine labels. It means 'the growing' or 'the making' of a wine and asserts that the wine concerned is from a specific vineyard. Under the Appellation Contrôlée rules, countless *crus* are classified in various hierarchical ranks. Hundreds of individual vineyards are described as *premier cru* or *grand cru* in the classic wine regions of Alsace, Bordeaux, Burgundy and Champagne. The common denominator is that the wine can be counted on to be expensive. On humbler wines, the use of the word *cru* tends to be mere decoration.

cru classé – *See* classed growth.

cuve – A vat for wine. French.

cuvée – French for the wine in a *cuve*, or vat. The word is much used on labels to imply that the wine is from just one vat, and thus of unique, unblended character. *Première cuvée* is supposedly the best wine from a given pressing because it comes from the free-run juice of grapes crushed by their own weight before pressing begins. Subsequent *cuvées* will have been from harsher pressings, grinding the grape pulp to extract the last drops of juice.

D

Dão – Major wine-producing region of northern Portugal now turning out much more interesting reds than it used to – worth looking out for anything made by mega-producer Sogrape.

demi sec – 'Half-dry' style of French (and some other) wines. Beware. It can mean anything from off-dry to cloyingly sweet.

DO – Denominación de Origen, Spain's wine-regulating scheme, similar to France's AC, but older – the first DO region was Rioja, from 1926. DO wines are Spain's best, accounting for a third of the nation's annual production.

DOC – Stands for Denominazione di Origine Controllata, Italy's equivalent of France's AC. The wines are made according to the stipulations of each of the system's 300-plus denominated zones of origin, along with a further 74 zones, which enjoy the superior classification of DOCG (DOC with *e Garantita* – guaranteed – appended).

DOCa – *Denominación de Origen Calificada* is Spain's highest regional wine classification; currently only Priorat and Rioja qualify.

DOP – Denominazione di Origine Protetta is an alternative classification to DOC (*qv*) under EU directive in Italy, comparable to AOP (*qv*) in France, but not yet widely adopted.

Durif – Rare black grape variety mostly of California, where it is also known as Petite Sirah, with some plantings in Australia.

E

earthy – A tricky word in the wine vocabulary. In this book, its use is meant to be complimentary. It indicates that the wine somehow suggests the soil the grapes were grown in, even (perhaps a shade too poetically) the landscape in which the vineyards lie. The amazing-value red wines of the torrid, volcanic southernmost regions of Italy are often described as earthy. This is an association with the pleasantly 'scorched' back-flavour in wines made from the ultra-ripe harvests of this near-sub-tropical part of the world.

edge – A wine with edge is one with evident (although not excessive) acidity.

élevé – 'Brought up' in French. Much used on wine labels where the wine has been matured (brought up) in oak barrels, *élevé en fûts de chêne*, to give it extra dimensions.

Entre Deux Mers – Meaning 'between two seas', it's a region lying between the Dordogne and Garonne rivers of Bordeaux, now mainly known for dry white wines from Sauvignon Blanc and Semillon grapes.

Estremadura – Wine-producing region occupying Portugal's coastal area north of Lisbon. Lots of interesting wines from indigenous grape varieties, often at bargain prices. If a label mentions Estremadura, it is a safe rule that there might be something good within.

Extremadura – Minor wine-producing region of western Spain abutting the frontier with Portugal's Alentejo region. Not to be confused with Estremadura of Portugal (above).

F

Falanghina – Revived ancient grape variety of southern Italy now making some superbly fresh and tangy white wines.

Faugères – AC of the Languedoc in south-west France. Source of many hearty, economic reds.

Feteasca – White grape variety widely grown in Romania. Name means 'maiden's grape' and the wine tends to be soft and slightly sweet.

Fiano – White grape variety of the Campania of southern Italy and Sicily, lately revived. It is said to have been cultivated by the ancient Romans for a wine called Apianum.

finish – The last flavour lingering in the mouth after wine has been swallowed.

fino – Pale and very dry style of sherry. You drink it thoroughly chilled – and you don't keep it any longer after opening than other dry white wines. Needs to be fresh to be at its best.

Fitou – AC of Languedoc, France. Red wines principally from Carignan, Grenache, Mourvèdre and Syrah grapes.

flabby – Fun word describing a wine that tastes dilute or watery, with insufficient acidity.

Frappato – Black grape variety of Sicily. Light red wines.

fruit – In tasting terms, the fruit is the greater part of the overall flavour of a wine. The wine is, after all, composed entirely of fruit

G

Gamay – The black grape that makes all red Beaujolais and some ordinary burgundy. It is a pretty safe rule to avoid Gamay wines from other regions.

Garganega – White grape variety of the Veneto region of north-east Italy. Best known as the principal ingredient of Soave, but occasionally included in varietal blends and mentioned as such on labels. Correctly pronounced 'gar-GAN-iga'.

Garnacha – Spanish black grape variety synonymous with Grenache of France. It is blended with Tempranillo to make the red wines of Rioja and Navarra, and is now quite widely cultivated elsewhere in Spain to make grippingly fruity varietals.

garrigue – Arid land of France's deep south giving its name to a style of red wine that notionally evokes the herby, heated, peppery flavours associated with such a landscape and its flora. A tricky metaphor.

Gavi – DOCG for dry aromatic white wine from Cortese grapes in Piedmont, north-west Italy. Trendy Gavi di Gavi wines tend to be enjoyably lush, but are rather expensive.

Gewürztraminer – One of the great grape varieties of Alsace, France. At their best, the wines are perfumed with lychees and are richly, spicily fruity, yet quite dry. Gewürztraminer from Alsace can be expensive, but the grape is also grown with some success in Germany, Italy, New Zealand and South America, at more approachable prices. Pronounced 'ge-VOORTS-traminner'.

Givry – AC for red and white wines in the Côte Chalonnaise sub-region of Burgundy. Source of some wonderfully natural-tasting reds that might be lighter than those of the more prestigious Côte d'Or to the north, but have great merits of their own. Relatively, the wines are often underpriced.

Glera – New official name for the Prosecco grape of northern Italy.

Godello – White grape variety of Galicia, Spain.

Graciano – Black grape variety of Spain that is one of the minor constituents of Rioja. Better known in its own right in Australia where it can make dense, spicy, long-lived red wines.

green – I don't often use this in the pejorative. Green, to me, is a likeable degree of freshness, especially in Sauvignon Blanc wines.

Grecanico – White grape variety of southern Italy, especially Sicily. Aromatic, grassy dry white wines.

Greco – White grape variety of southern Italy believed to be of ancient Greek origin. Big-flavoured dry white wines.

Grenache – The mainstay of the wines of the southern Rhône Valley in France. Grenache is usually the greater part of the mix in Côtes du Rhône reds and is widely planted right across the neighbouring Languedoc-Roussillon region. It's a big-cropping variety that thrives even in the hottest climates and is really a blending grape – most commonly with Syrah, the noble variety of the northern Rhône. Few French wines are labelled with its name, but the grape has caught on in Australia in a big way and it is now becoming a familiar varietal, known for strong, dark liquorous reds. Grenache is the French name for what is originally a Spanish variety, Garnacha.

Grillo – White grape of Sicily said to be among the island's oldest indigenous varieties, pre-dating the arrival of the Greeks in 600 BC. Much used for fortified Marsala, it has lately been revived for interesting, aromatic dry table wines.

grip – In wine-tasting terminology, the sensation in the mouth produced by a wine that has a healthy quantity of tannin in it. A wine with grip is a good wine. A wine with too much tannin, or which is still too young (the tannin hasn't 'softened' with age) is not described as having grip, but as mouth-puckering – or simply undrinkable.

Grolleau – Black grape variety of the Loire Valley principally cultivated for Rosé d'Anjou.

Gros Plant – White grape variety of the Pays Nantais in France's Loire estuary; synonymous with the Folle Blanche grape of south-west France.

Grüner Veltliner – The 'national' white-wine grape of Austria. In the past it made mostly soft, German-style everyday wines, but now is behind some excellent dry styles, too.

H

halbtrocken – 'Half-dry' in Germany's wine vocabulary. A reassurance that the wine is not a sugared Liebfraumilch-style confection.

hard – In red wine, a flavour denoting excess tannin, probably due to immaturity.

Haut-Médoc – Extensive AC of Bordeaux accounting for the greater part of the vineyard area to the north of the city of Bordeaux west of the Gironde river. The Haut-Médoc incorporates the prestigious commune-ACs of Listrac, Margaux, Moulis, Pauillac, St Estèphe and St Julien.

Hermitage – AC of northern Rhône Valley, France for red wines from Syrah grapes and some whites. Hermitage is also the regional name in South Africa for the Cinsaut grape.

hock – The wine of Germany's Rhine river valleys. Traditionally, but no longer consistently, it comes in brown bottles, as distinct from the wine of the Mosel river valleys – which comes in green ones.

Hunter Valley – Long-established (1820s) wine-producing region of New South Wales, Australia.

I

Indicación Geográfica Protegida (IGP) – Spain's country-wine quality designation covers 46 zones across the country. Wines made under the IGP can be labelled Vino de la Tierra.

Indication Géographique Protégée (IGP) – Introduced to France in 2010 under EU-wide wine-designation rules, IGP covers the wines previously known as vins de pays. Some wines are currently labelled IGP, but established vins de pays producers are redesignating slowly, if at all, and are not obliged to do so. Some will abbreviate, so, for example, Vin de Pays d'Oc shortens to Pays d'Oc.

Indicazione Geografica Tipica (IGT) – Italian wine-quality designation, broadly equivalent to France's IGP. The label has to state the geographical location of the vineyard and will often (but not always) state the principal grape varieties from which the wine is made.

isinglass – A gelatinous material used in fining (clarifying) wine. It is derived from fish bladders and consequently is eschewed by makers of 'vegetarian' or 'vegan' wines.

J

jammy – The 'sweetness' in dry red wines is supposed to evoke ripeness rather than sugariness. Sometimes, flavours include a sweetness reminiscent of jam. Usually a fault in the winemaking technique.

Jerez – Wine town of Andalucia, Spain, and home to sherry. The English word 'sherry' is a simple mispronunciation of Jerez.

joven – Young wine, Spanish. In regions such as Rioja, *vino joven* is a synonym for *sin crianza*, which means 'without ageing' in cask or bottle.

Jura – Wine region of eastern France incorporating four AOCs, Arbois, Château-Chalon, Côtes du Jura and L'Etoile. Known for still red, white and rosé wines and sparkling wines as well as exotic *vin de paille* and *vin jaune*.

Jurançon – Appellation for white wines from Courbu and Manseng grapes at Pau, south-west France.

K

Kabinett – Under Germany's bewildering wine-quality rules, this is a classification of a top-quality (QmP) wine. Expect a keen, dry, racy style. The name comes from the cabinet or cupboard in which winemakers traditionally kept their most treasured bottles.

Kekfrankos – Black grape variety of Hungary, particularly the Sopron region, which makes some of the country's more interesting red wines, characterised by colour and spiciness. Same variety as Austria's Blaufrankisch.

L

Ladoix – Unfashionable AC at northern edge of Côtes de Beaune makes some of Burgundy's true bargain reds. A name to look out for.

Lambrusco – The name is that of a black grape variety widely grown across northern Italy. True Lambrusco wine is red, dry and very slightly sparkling, and enjoying a current vogue in Britain.

Languedoc-Roussillon – Extensive wine region of southern France incorporating numerous ACs and IGP zones, notably the Pays d'Oc and Côtes de Roussillon.

lees – The detritus of the winemaking process that collects in the bottom of the vat or cask. Wines left for extended periods on the lees can acquire extra dimensions of flavour, in particular a 'leesy' creaminess.

legs – The liquid residue left clinging to the sides of the glass after wine has been swirled. The persistence of the legs is an indicator of the weight of alcohol. Also known as 'tears'.

lieu dit – This is starting to appear on French wine labels. It translates as an 'agreed place' and is an area of vineyard defined as of particular character or merit, but not classified under wine law. Usually, the *lieu dit*'s name is stated, with the implication that the wine in question has special merit.

liquorice – The pungent, slightly burnt flavours of this confection are detectable in some wines made from very ripe grapes, for example, the Malbec harvested in Argentina and several varieties grown in the very hot vineyards of southernmost Italy. A close synonym is 'tarry'. This characteristic is by no means a fault in red wine, unless very dominant, but it can make for a challenging flavour that might not appeal to all tastes.

liquorous – Wines of great weight and glyceriney texture (evidenced by the 'legs', or 'tears', which cling to the glass after the wine has been swirled) are always noteworthy. The connection with liquor is drawn in respect of the feel of the wine in the mouth, rather than with the higher alcoholic strength of spirits.

Lirac – Village and AC of southern Rhône Valley, France. A near-neighbour of the esteemed appellation of Châteauneuf du Pape, Lirac makes red wine of comparable depth and complexity, at competitive prices.

Lugana – DOC of Lombardy, Italy, known for a dry white wine that is often of real distinction – rich, almondy stuff from the ubiquitous Trebbiano grape.

M

Macabeo – One of the main grapes used for cava, the sparkling wine of Spain. It is the same grape as Viura.

Mâcon – Town and collective appellation of southern Burgundy, France. Minerally white wines from Chardonnay grapes and light reds from Pinot Noir and some Gamay. The better ones, and the ones exported, have the AC Mâcon-Villages and there are individual village wines with their own ACs including Mâcon-Clessé, Mâcon-Viré and Mâcon-Lugny.

Malbec – Black grape variety grown on a small scale in Bordeaux, and the mainstay of the wines of Cahors in France's Dordogne region under the name Cot. Now much better known for producing big butch reds in Argentina.

malolactic fermentation – In winemaking, a common natural bacterial action following alcoholic fermentation, converting malic (apple) acid into lactic (milk) acid. The effect is to reduce tartness and to boost creaminess in the wine. Adding lactic bacteria to wine to promote the process is widely practised.

manzanilla – Pale, very dry sherry of Sanlucar de Barrameda, a resort town on the Bay of Cadiz in Spain. Manzanilla is proud to be distinct from the pale, very dry fino sherry of the main producing town of Jerez de la Frontera an hour's drive inland. Drink it chilled and fresh – it goes downhill in an opened bottle after just a few days, even if kept (as it should be) in the fridge.

Margaret River – Vineyard region of Western Australia regarded as ideal for grape varieties including Cabernet Sauvignon. It has a relatively cool climate and a reputation for making sophisticated wines, both red and white.

Marlborough – Best-known vineyard region of New Zealand's South Island has a cool climate and a name for brisk but cerebral Sauvignon Blanc and Chardonnay wines.

Marsanne – White grape variety of the northern Rhône Valley and, increasingly, of the wider south of France. It's known for making well-coloured wines with heady aroma and nuanced fruit.

Mataro – Black grape variety of Australia. It's the same as the Mourvèdre of France and Monastrell of Spain.

Mazuelo – Spanish name for France's black grape variety Carignan.

McLaren Vale – Vineyard region south of Adelaide in south-east Australia. Known for blockbuster Shiraz (and Chardonnay) that can be of great balance and quality from winemakers who manage to keep the ripeness under control.

meaty – In wine-tasting, a weighty, rich red wine style.

Mencia – Black grape variety of Galicia and north-west Spain. Light red wines.

Mendoza – Wine region of Argentina. Lying to the east of the Andes mountains, just about opposite the best vineyards of Chile on the other side, Mendoza accounts for the bulk of Argentine wine production.

Merlot – One of the great black wine grapes of Bordeaux, and now grown all over the world. The name is said to derive from the French *merle*, a blackbird. Characteristics of Merlot-based wines attract descriptions such as 'plummy' and 'plump' with black-cherry aromas. The grapes are larger than most, and thus have less skin in proportion to their flesh. This means the resulting wines have less tannin than wines from smaller-berry varieties such as Cabernet Sauvignon, and are therefore, in the Bordeaux context at least, more suitable for drinking while still relatively young.

middle palate – In wine-tasting, the impression given by the wine after the first impact on 'entry' and before the 'finish' when the wine is swallowed.

Midi – Catch-all term for the deep south of France west of the Rhône Valley.

mineral – Irresistible term in wine-tasting. To me it evokes flavours such as the stone-pure freshness of some Loire dry whites, or the flinty quality of the more austere style of the Chardonnay grape, especially in Chablis. Mineral really just means something mined, as in dug out of the ground, like iron ore (as in 'steely' whites) or rock, as in, er, stone. Maybe there's something in it, but I am not entirely confident.

Minervois – AC for (mostly) red wines from vineyards around the Roman-founded town of Minerve in the Languedoc-Roussillon region of France. Often good value. The recently elevated Minervois La Livinière AC is a sort of Minervois *grand cru*.

Monastrell – Black grape variety of Spain, widely planted in Mediterranean regions for inexpensive wines notable for their high alcohol and toughness – though they can mature into excellent, soft reds. The variety is known in France as Mourvèdre and in Australia as Mataro.

Monbazillac – AC for sweet, dessert wines within the wider appellation of Bergerac in south-west France. Made from the same grape varieties (principally Sauvignon and Semillon) that go into the much costlier counterpart wines of Barsac and Sauternes near Bordeaux, these stickies from botrytis-affected, late-harvested grapes can be delicious and good value for money.

Montalcino – Hill town of Tuscany, Italy, and a DOCG for strong and very long-lived red wines from Brunello grapes. The wines are mostly very expensive. Rosso di Montalcino, a DOC for the humbler wines of the zone, is often a good buy.

Montepulciano – Black grape variety of Italy. Best known in Montepulciano d'Abruzzo, the juicy, purply-black and bramble-fruited red of the Abruzzi region midway down Italy's Adriatic side. Also the grape in the rightly popular hearty reds of Rosso Conero from around Ancona in the Marches. Not to be confused with the hill town of Montepulciano in Tuscany, famous for expensive Vino Nobile di Montepulciano wine, made from Sangiovese grapes.

morello – Lots of red wines have smells and flavours redolent of cherries. Morello cherries, among the darkest coloured and sweetest of all varieties and the preferred choice of cherry-brandy producers, have a distinct sweetness resembled by some wines made from Merlot grapes. A morello whiff or taste is generally very welcome.

Moscatel – Spanish Muscat.

Moscato – *See* Muscat.

moselle – The wine of Germany's Mosel river valleys, collectively known for winemaking purposes as the Mosel-Saar-Ruwer. The wine always comes in slim, green bottles, as distinct from the brown bottles traditionally, but no longer exclusively, employed for Rhine wines.

Mourvèdre – Widely planted black grape variety of southern France. It's an ingredient in many of the wines of Provence, the Rhône and Languedoc, including the ubiquitous Pays d'Oc. It's a hot-climate vine and the wine is usually blended with other varieties to give sweet aromas and 'backbone' to the mix. Known as Mataro in Australia and Monastrell in Spain.

Muscadet – One of France's most familiar everyday whites, made from a grape called the Melon or Melon de Bourgogne. It comes from vineyards at the estuarial end of the River Loire, and has a sea-breezy freshness about it. The better wines are reckoned to be those from the vineyards in the Sèvre et Maine region, and many are made *sur lie* – 'on the lees' – meaning that the wine is left in contact with the yeasty deposit of its fermentation until just before bottling, in an endeavour to add interest to what can sometimes be an acidic and fruitless style.

Muscat – Grape variety with origins in ancient Greece, and still grown widely among the Aegean islands for the production of sweet white wines. Muscats are the wines that taste more like grape juice than any other – but the high sugar levels ensure they are also among the most alcoholic of wines, too. Known as Moscato in Italy, the grape is much used for making sweet sparkling wines, as in Asti Spumante or Moscato d'Asti. There are several appellations in south-west France for inexpensive Muscats made rather like port, part-fermented before the addition of grape alcohol to halt the conversion of sugar into alcohol, creating a sweet and heady *vin doux naturel*. Dry Muscat wines, when well made, have a delicious sweet aroma but a refreshing, light touch with flavours reminiscent variously of orange blossom, wood smoke and grapefruit.

must – New-pressed grape juice prior to fermentation.

N

Navarra – DO wine-producing region of northern Spain adjacent to, and overshadowed by, Rioja. Navarra's wines can be startlingly akin to their neighbouring rivals, and sometimes rather better value for money.

négociant – In France, a dealer-producer who buys wines from growers and matures and/or blends them for bottling and sale under his or her own label. Purists can be a bit sniffy about these entrepreneurs, claiming that only the vine-grower with his or her own winemaking set-up can make truly authentic stuff, but the truth is that many of the best wines of France are *négociant*-produced – especially at the humbler end of the price scale. *Négociants* are often identified on wine labels as *négociant-éleveur* (literally 'dealer-bringer-up'), meaning that the wine has been matured, blended and bottled by the party in question.

Negroamaro – Black grape variety mainly of Puglia, the much-lauded wine region of south-east Italy. Dense, earthy red wines with ageing potential and plenty of alcohol. The name is probably (if not obviously) derived from Italian *negro* (black) and *amaro* (bitter). The grape behind Copertino, Salice Salentino and Squinzano.

Nerello Mascalese – Black grape of Sicily, most prolific in vineyards surrounding Mount Etna, making distinctive, flavoursome reds.

Nero d'Avola – Black grape variety of Sicily (Avola is a town in the province of Syracuse) and southern Italy. It makes deep-coloured wines that, given half a chance, can develop intensity and richness with age.

non-vintage – A wine is described as such when it has been blended from the harvests of more than one year. A non-vintage wine is not necessarily an inferior one, but under quality-control regulations around the world, still table wines most usually derive solely from one year's grape crop to qualify for appellation status. Champagnes and sparkling wines are mostly blended from several vintages, as are fortified wines such as port and sherry.

nose – In the vocabulary of the wine-taster, the nose is the scent of a wine. Sounds a bit dotty, but it makes a sensible enough alternative to the rather bald 'smell'. The use of the word 'perfume' implies that the wine smells particularly good. 'Aroma' is used specifically to describe a wine that smells as it should, as in 'this burgundy has the authentic strawberry-raspberry aroma of Pinot Noir'.

O

oak – Most of the world's costliest wines are matured in new or nearly new oak barrels, giving additional opulence of flavour. Of late, many cheaper wines have been getting the oak treatment, too, in older, cheaper casks, or simply by having sacks of oak chippings poured into their steel or fibreglass holding tanks. 'Oak aged' on a label is likely to indicate the latter treatments. But the overtly oaked wines of Australia have in some cases been so overdone that there is now a reactive trend whereby some producers proclaim their wines – particularly Chardonnays – as 'unoaked' on the label, thereby asserting that the flavours are more naturally achieved.

Oltrepo Pavese – Wine-producing zone of Piedmont, north-west Italy. The name means 'south of Pavia across the [river] Po' and the wines, both white and red, can be excellent quality and value for money.

organic wine – As in other sectors of the food industry, demand for organically made wine is – or appears to be – growing. As a rule, a wine qualifies as organic if it comes entirely from grapes grown in vineyards cultivated without the use of synthetic materials, and made in a winery where chemical treatments or additives are shunned with similar vigour. In fact, there are plenty of winemakers in the world using organic methods, but who disdain to label their bottles as such. Wines proclaiming their organic status used to carry the same sort of premium as their counterparts round the corner in the fruit, vegetable and meat aisles. But organic viticulture is now commonplace and there seems little price impact. There is no single worldwide (or even Europe-wide) standard for organic food or wine, so you pretty much have to take the producer's word for it.

P

Pasqua – One of the biggest and, it should be said, best wine producers of the Veneto region of north-west Italy.

Passerina – White grape variety of Marche, Italy. Used in blending but there is also a regional Passerina DOC.

Passetoutgrains – Designation for wine made from more than one grape variety grown in the same vineyard. French. Mostly red burgundy from Gamay and Pinot Noir.

Pays d'Oc – Shortened form under recent rule changes of French wine designation Vin de Pays d'Oc. All other similar regional designations can be similarly abbreviated.

Pecorino – White grape variety of mid-eastern Italy currently in vogue for well-coloured dry white varietal wines.

Periquita – Black grape variety of southern Portugal. Makes rather exotic spicy reds. Name means 'parrot'.

Perricone – Black grape variety of Sicily. Low-acid red wines.

PET – It's what they call plastic wine bottles – lighter to transport and allegedly as ecological as glass. Polyethylene terephthalate.

Petit Verdot – Black grape variety of Bordeaux contributing additional colour, density and spiciness to Cabernet Sauvignon-dominated blends. Mostly a minority player at home, but in Australia and California it is grown as the principal variety for some big hearty reds of real character.

petrol – When white wines from certain grapes, especially Riesling, are allowed to age in the bottle for longer than a year or two, they can take on a spirity aroma reminiscent of petrol or diesel. In grand mature German wines, this is considered a good thing.

Picpoul – Grape variety of southern France. Best known in Picpoul de Pinet, a dry white from near Sète on the Golfe de Lyon, lately elevated to AOP status. The name Picpoul (also Piquepoul) means 'stings the lips' – referring to the natural high acidity of the juice.

Piemonte – North-western province of Italy, which we call Piedmont, known for the spumante wines of the town of Asti, plus expensive Barbaresco and Barolo and better-value varietal red wines from Nebbiolo, Barbera and Dolcetto grapes.

Pinotage – South Africa's own black grape variety. Makes red wines ranging from light and juicy to dark, strong and long-lived. It's a cross between Pinot Noir and a grape the South Africans used to call Hermitage (thus the portmanteau name) but turns out to have been Cinsault.

Pinot Blanc – White grape variety principally of Alsace, France. Florally perfumed, exotically fruity dry white wines.

Pinot Grigio – White grape variety of northern Italy. Wines bearing its name are perplexingly fashionable. Good examples have an interesting smoky-pungent aroma and keen, slaking fruit. But most are dull. Originally French, it is at its best in the lushly exotic Pinot Gris wines of Alsace and is also successfully cultivated in Germany and New Zealand.

Pinot Noir – The great black grape of Burgundy, France. It makes all the region's fabulously expensive red wines. Notoriously difficult to grow in warmer climates, it is nevertheless cultivated by countless intrepid winemakers in the New World intent on reproducing the magic appeal of red burgundy. California and New Zealand have come closest. Some Chilean Pinot Noirs are inexpensive and worth trying.

Pouilly Fuissé – Village and AC of the Mâconnais region of southern Burgundy in France. Dry white wines from Chardonnay grapes. Wines are among the highest rated of the Mâconnais.

Pouilly Fumé – Village and AC of the Loire Valley in France. Dry white wines from Sauvignon Blanc grapes. Similar 'pebbly', 'grassy' or 'gooseberry' style to neighbouring AC Sancerre. The notion put about by some enthusiasts that Pouilly Fumé is 'smoky' is surely nothing more than word association with the name.

Primitivo – Black grape variety of southern Italy, especially the region of Puglia. Named from Latin *primus* for first, the grape is among the earliest-ripening of all varieties. The wines are typically dense and dark in colour with plenty of alcohol, and have an earthy, spicy style.

Priorat – Emerging wine region of Catalonia, Spain. Highly valued red wines from Garnacha and other varieties. Generic brands available in supermarkets are well worth trying out.

Prosecco – Softly sparkling wine of Italy's Veneto region. The best come from the DOCG Conegliano-Valdobbiadene, made as spumante ('foaming') wines in pressurised tanks, typically to 11 per cent alcohol and ranging from softly sweet to crisply dry. The constituent grape, previously also known as Prosecco, has been officially assigned the name Glera.

Puglia – The region occupying the 'heel' of southern Italy, making many good, inexpensive wines from indigenous grape varieties.

Q

QbA – German, standing for Qualitätswein bestimmter Anbaugebiete. It means 'quality wine from designated areas' and implies that the wine is made from grapes with a minimum level of ripeness, but it's by no means a guarantee of exciting quality. Only wines labelled QmP (see next entry) can be depended upon to be special.

QmP – Stands for Qualitätswein mit Prädikat. These are the serious wines of Germany, made without the addition of sugar to 'improve' them. To qualify for QmP status, the grapes must reach a level of ripeness as measured on a sweetness scale – all according to Germany's fiendishly complicated wine-quality regulations. Wines from grapes that reach the stated minimum level of sweetness qualify for the description of Kabinett. The next level up earns the rank of Spätlese, meaning 'late-picked'. Kabinett wines can be expected to be dry and brisk in style, and Spätlese wines a little bit riper and fuller. The next grade up, Auslese, meaning 'selected harvest', indicates a wine made from super-ripe grapes; it will be golden in colour and honeyed in flavour. A generation ago, these wines were as valued, and as expensive, as any of the world's grandest appellations. Beerenauslese and Trockenbeerenauslese are speciality wines made from individually picked late-harvest grapes.

Quincy – AC of Loire Valley, France, known for pebbly-dry white wines from Sauvignon grapes. The wines are forever compared to those of nearby and much better-known Sancerre – and Quincy often represents better value for money. Pronounced 'KAN-see'.

Quinta – Portuguese for farm or estate. It precedes the names of many of Portugal's best-known wines. It is pronounced 'KEEN-ta'.

R

racy – Evocative wine-tasting description for wine that thrills the tastebuds with a rush of exciting sensations. Good Rieslings often qualify.

raisiny – Wines from grapes that have been very ripe or overripe at harvest can take on a smell and flavour akin to the concentrated, heat-dried sweetness of raisins. As a minor element in the character of a wine, this can add to the appeal but as a dominant characteristic it is a fault.

rancio – Spanish term harking back to Roman times when wines were commonly stored in jars outside, exposed to the sun, so they oxidised and took on a burnt sort of flavour. Today, *rancio* describes a baked – and by no means unpleasant – flavour in fortified wines, particularly sherry and Madeira.

Reserva – In Portugal and Spain, this has genuine significance. The Portuguese use it for special wines with a higher alcohol level and longer ageing, although the precise periods vary between regions. In Spain, especially in the Navarra and Rioja regions, it means the wine must have had at least a year in oak and two in bottle before release.

reserve – On French (as *réserve*) or other wines, this implies special-quality, longer-aged wines, but has no official significance.

residual sugar – There is sugar in all wine, left over from the fermentation process. Some producers now mention the quantity of residual sugar on back labels in grams per litre of wine, even though so far there is no legal obligation to do so. Dry wines, red or white, typically have 3 g/l or fewer. Above that, you might well be able to taste the sweetness. In southern hemisphere wines, made from grapes that have ripened under more-intense sunlight than their European counterparts, sugar levels can be correspondingly higher. Sweet wines such as Sauternes contain up to 150 g/l. Dry ('brut') sparkling wines made by the 'champagne' method typically have 10 g/l and tank-method fizzes such as prosecco up to 15 g/l.

Retsina – The universal white wine of Greece. It has been traditionally made in Attica, the region of Athens, for a very long time, and is said to owe its origins and name to the ancient custom of sealing amphorae (terracotta jars) of the wine with a gum made from pine resin. Some of the flavour of the resin inevitably transmitted itself into the wine, and ancient Greeks acquired a lasting taste for it.

Reuilly – AC of Loire Valley, France, for crisp dry whites from Sauvignon grapes. Pronounced 'RER-yee'.

Ribatejo – Emerging wine region of Portugal. Worth seeking out on labels of red wines in particular, because new winemakers are producing lively stuff from distinctive indigenous grapes such as Castelao and Trincadeira.

Ribera del Duero – Classic wine region of north-west Spain lying along the River Duero (which crosses the border to become Portugal's Douro, forming the valley where port comes from). It is home to an estate oddly named Vega Sicilia, where red wines of epic quality are made and sold at equally epic prices. Further down the scale, some very good reds are made, too.

Riesling – The noble grape variety of Germany. It is correctly pronounced 'REEZ-ling', not 'RICE-ling'. Once notorious as the grape behind all those boring 'medium' Liebfraumilches and Niersteiners, this grape has had a bad press. In fact, there has never been much, if any, Riesling in German plonk. But the country's best wines, the so-called Qualitätswein mit Prädikat grades, are made almost exclusively with Riesling. These wines range from crisply fresh and appley styles to extravagantly fruity, honeyed wines from late-harvested grapes. Excellent Riesling wines are also made in Alsace and now in Australasia.

Rioja – The principal fine-wine region of Spain, in the country's north east. The pricier wines are noted for their vanilla-pod richness from long ageing in oak casks. Tempranillo and Garnacha grapes make the reds, Viura the whites.

Ripasso – A particular style of Valpolicella wine. New wine is partially refermented in vats that have been used to make Recioto reds (wines made from semi-dried grapes), thus creating a bigger, smoother version of usually light and pale Valpolicella.

Riserva – In Italy, a wine made only in the best vintages, and allowed longer ageing in cask and bottle.

Rivaner – Alternative name for Germany's Müller-Thurgau grape.

Riverland – Vineyard region to the immediate north of the Barossa Valley of South Australia, extending east into New South Wales.

Roditis – White grape variety of Greece, known for fresh dry whites with decent acidity, often included in retsina.

rosso – Red wine, Italy.

Rosso Conero – DOC red wine made in the environs of Ancona in the Marches, Italy. Made from the Montepulciano grape, the wine can provide excellent value for money.

Ruby Cabernet – Black grape variety of California, created by crossing Cabernet Sauvignon and Carignan. Makes soft and squelchy red wine at home and in South Africa.

Rueda – DO of north-west Spain making first-class refreshing dry whites from the indigenous Verdejo grape, imported Sauvignon, and others. Exciting quality, and prices are keen.

Rully – AC of Chalonnais region of southern Burgundy, France. White wines from Chardonnay and red wines from Pinot Noir grapes. Both can be very good and substantially cheaper than their more northerly Burgundian neighbours. Pronounced 'ROO-yee'.

S

Sagrantino – Black grape variety native to Perugia, Italy. Dark, tannic wines best known in DOCG Sagrantino de Montefalco. Now also cultivated in Australia.

Saint Emilion – AC of Bordeaux, France. Centred on the romantic hill town of St Emilion, this famous sub-region makes some of the grandest red wines of France, but also some of the best-value ones. Less fashionable than the Médoc region on the opposite (west) bank of the River Gironde that bisects Bordeaux, St Emilion wines are made largely with the Merlot grape, and are relatively quick to mature. The top wines are classified *1er grand cru classé* and are madly expensive, but many more are classified respectively *grand cru classé* and *grand cru*, and these designations can be seen as a fairly trustworthy indicator of quality. There are several 'satellite' St Emilion ACs named after the villages at their centres, notably Lussac St Emilion, Montagne St Emilion and Puisseguin St Emilion. Some excellent wines are made by estates within these ACs, and at relatively affordable prices thanks to the comparatively humble status of their satellite designations.

Salento – Up-and-coming wine region of southern Italy. Many good bargain reds from local grapes including Nero d'Avola and Primitivo.

Sancerre – AC of the Loire Valley, France, renowned for flinty-fresh Sauvignon Blanc whites and rarer Pinot Noir reds and rosés.

Sangiovese – The local black grape of Tuscany, Italy, is the principal variety used for Chianti. Also planted further south in Italy and in the New World. Generic Sangiovese di Toscana can make a consoling substitute for costly Chianti.

Saumur – Town and appellation of Loire Valley, France. Characterful minerally red wines from Cabernet Franc grapes, and some whites. Sparkling wines from Chenin Blanc grapes can be good value.

Saumur-Champigny – Separate appellation for red wines from Cabernet Franc grapes of Saumur in the Loire, sometimes very good and lively.

Sauvignon Blanc – French white grape variety now grown worldwide. New Zealand has raised worldwide production values challenging the long supremacy of French ACs in Bordeaux and the Loire Valley. Chile and South Africa aspire similarly. The wines are characterised by aromas of gooseberry, peapod, fresh-cut grass, even asparagus. Flavours are often described as 'grassy' or 'nettly'.

sec – Dry wine style. French.

secco – Dry wine style. Italian.

seco – Dry wine style. Spanish.

Semillon – White grape variety originally of Bordeaux, where it is blended with Sauvignon Blanc to make fresh dry whites and, when harvested very late in the season, the ambrosial sweet whites of Barsac, Sauternes and other appellations. Even in the driest wines, the grape can be recognised from its honeyed, sweet-pineapple, even banana-like aromas. Now widely planted in Australia and Latin America, and frequently blended with Chardonnay to make dry whites, some of them interesting.

sherry – The great aperitif wine of Spain, centred on the Andalusian city of Jerez (the name 'sherry' is an English mispronunciation). There is a lot of sherry-style wine in the world, but only the authentic wine from Jerez and the neighbouring producing centres of Puerta de Santa Maria and Sanlucar de Barrameda may label their wines as such. The Spanish drink real sherry – very dry and fresh, pale in colour and served well-chilled – called fino and manzanilla, and darker but naturally dry variations called amontillado, palo cortado and oloroso.

Shiraz – Australian name for the Syrah grape. The variety is the most widely planted of any in Australia, and makes red wines of wildly varying quality, characterised by dense colour, high alcohol, spicy fruit and generous, cushiony texture.

Somontano – Wine region of north-east Spain. Name means 'under the mountains' – in this case the Pyrenees – and the region has had DO status since 1984. Much innovative winemaking here, with New World styles emerging. Some very good buys. A region to watch.

souple – French wine-tasting term that translates into English as 'supple' or even 'docile' as in 'pliable', but I understand it in the vinous context to mean muscular but soft – a wine with tannin as well as soft fruit.

Spätlese – *See* QmP.

spirity – Some wines, mostly from the New World, are made from grapes so ripe at harvest that their high alcohol content can be detected through a mildly burning sensation on the tongue, similar to the effect of sipping a spirit. Young Port wines can be detectably spirity.

spritzy – Describes a wine with a gentle sparkle. Some young wines are intended to have this elusive fizziness; in others it is a fault.

spumante – Sparkling wine of Italy. Asti Spumante is the best known, from the town of Asti in the north-west Italian province of Piemonte. Many Prosecco wines are labelled as Spumante in style. The term describes wines that are fully sparkling. Frizzante wines have a less vigorous mousse.

stalky – A useful tasting term to describe red wines with flavours that make you think the stalks from the grape bunches must have been fermented along with the must (juice). Red Loire wines and youthful claret very often have this mild astringency. In moderation it's fine, but if it dominates it probably signifies the wine is at best immature and at worst badly made.

Stellenbosch – Town and region at the heart of South Africa's wine industry. It's an hour's drive from Cape Town and the source of much of the country's cheaper wine. Some serious-quality estate wines as well.

stony – Wine-tasting term for keenly dry white wines. It's meant to indicate a wine of purity and real quality, with just the right match of fruit and acidity.

structured – Good wines are not one-dimensional, they have layers of flavour and texture. A structured wine has phases of enjoyment: the 'attack', or first impression in the mouth; the middle palate as the wine is held in the mouth; and the lingering aftertaste.

sugar – *See* residual sugar.

sulphites – Nearly all wines, barring some esoteric 'natural' types of a kind not found in supermarkets are made with the aid of preparations containing sulphur to combat diseases in the vineyards and bacterial infections in the winery. It's difficult to make wine without sulphur. Even 'organic' wines need it. Because some people are sensitive to the traces of sulphur in some wines, worldwide health authorities insist wine labels bear the warning 'Contains sulphites'.

summer fruit – Wine-tasting term intended to convey a smell or taste of soft fruits such as strawberries and raspberries – without having to commit too specifically to which.

superiore – On labels of Italian wines, this is more than an idle boast. Under DOC(G) rules, wines must qualify for the *superiore* designation by reaching one or more specified quality levels, usually a higher alcohol content or an additional period of maturation. Frascati, for example, qualifies for DOC status at 11.5 per cent alcohol, but to be classified *superiore* must have 12 per cent alcohol.

sur lie – Literally, 'on the lees'. It's a term now widely used on the labels of Muscadet wines, signifying that after fermentation has died down, the new wine has been left in the tank over the winter on the lees – the detritus of yeasts and other interesting compounds left over from the turbid fermentation process. The idea is that additional interest is imparted into the flavour of the wine.

Syrah – The noble grape of the Rhône Valley, France. Makes very dark, dense wine characterised by peppery, tarry aromas. Now planted all over southern France and farther afield. In Australia it is known as Shiraz.

T

table wine – Wine that is unfortified and of an alcoholic strength, for UK tax purposes anyway, of no more than 15 per cent. I use the term to distinguish, for example, between the red table wines of the Douro Valley in Portugal and the region's better-known fortified wine, port.

Tafelwein – Table wine, German. The humblest quality designation, which doesn't usually bode very well.

tank method – Bulk-production process for sparkling wines. Base wine undergoes secondary fermentation in a large, sealed vat rather than in individual closed bottles. Also known as the Charmat method after the name of the inventor of the process. Prosecco is made by the tank method.

Tai – White grape variety of north-east Italy, a relative of Sauvignon Blanc. Also known in Italy as Tocai Friulano or, more correctly, Friulano.

Tannat – Black grape of south-west France, notably for wines of Madiran, and lately named as the variety most beneficial to health thanks to its outstanding antioxidant content.

tannin – Well known as the film-forming, teeth-coating component in tea, tannin is a natural compound that occurs in black grape skins and acts as a natural preservative in wine. Its noticeable presence in wine is regarded as a good thing. It gives young everyday reds their dryness, firmness of flavour and backbone. And it helps high-quality reds to retain their lively fruitiness for many years. A grand Bordeaux red when first made, for example, will have purply-sweet, rich fruit and mouth-puckering tannin, but after ten years or so this will have evolved into a delectably fruity, mature wine in which the formerly parching effects of the tannin have receded almost completely, leaving the shade of 'residual tannin' that marks out a great wine approaching maturity.

Tarrango – Black grape variety of Australia.

tarry – On the whole, winemakers don't like critics to say their wines evoke the redolence of road repairs, but I can't help using this term to describe the agreeable, sweet, 'burnt' flavour that is often found at the centre of the fruit in red wines from Argentina, Italy, Portugal and South Africa in particular.

TCA – Dreaded ailment in wine, usually blamed on faulty corks. It stands for 246 *trichloroanisol* and is characterised by a horrible musty smell and flavour in the affected wine. Thanks to technological advances made by cork manufacturers in Portugal – the leading cork nation – TCA is now in retreat.

tears – The colourless alcohol in the wine left clinging to the inside of the glass after the contents have been swirled. Persistent tears (also known as 'legs') indicate a wine of good concentration.

Tempranillo – The great black grape of Spain. Along with Garnacha (Grenache in France) it makes most red Rioja and Navarra wines and, under many pseudonyms, is an important or exclusive contributor to the wines of many other regions of Spain. It is also widely cultivated in South America.

Teroldego – Black grape variety of Trentino, northern Italy. Often known as Teroldego Rotaliano after the Rotaliano region where most of the vineyards lie. Deep-coloured, assertive, green-edged red wines.

terroir – French word for 'ground' or 'soil' has mystical meaning in vineyard country. Winemakers attribute the distinct characteristics of their products, not just to the soil conditions but to the lie of the land and the prevailing (micro)climate, all within the realm of terroir. The word now frequently appears on effusive back labels asserting the unique appeal of the wine. Some critics scoff that terroir is all imagined nonsense.

tinto – On Spanish labels indicates a deeply coloured red wine. Clarete denotes a paler colour. Also Portuguese.

Toro – Quality wine region east of Zamora, Spain.

Torrontes – White grape variety of Argentina. Makes soft, dry wines often with delicious grapey-spicy aroma, similar in style to the classic dry Muscat wines of Alsace, but at more accessible prices.

Touraine – Region encompassing a swathe of the Loire Valley, France. Non-AC wines may be labelled 'Sauvignon de Touraine'.

Touriga Nacional – The most valued black grape variety of the Douro Valley in Portugal, where port is made. The name Touriga now appears on an increasing number of table wines made as sidelines by the port producers. They can be very good, with the same spirity aroma and sleek flavours of port itself, minus the fortification.

Traminer – Grape variety, the same as Gewürztraminer.

Trebbiano – The workhorse white grape of Italy. A productive variety that is easy to cultivate, it seems to be included in just about every ordinary white wine of the entire nation – including Frascati, Orvieto and Soave. It is the same grape as France's Ugni Blanc. There are, however, distinct regional variations of the grape. Trebbiano di Lugana (also known as Turbiana) makes a distinctive white in the DOC of the name, sometimes very good, while Trebbiano di Toscana makes a major contribution to the distinctly less interesting dry whites of Chianti country.

Trincadeira Preta – Portuguese black grape variety native to the port-producing vineyards of the Douro Valley (where it goes under the name Tinta Amarella). In southern Portugal, it produces dark and sturdy table wines.

trocken – 'Dry' German wine. The description does have a particular meaning under German wine law, namely that there is only a low level of unfermented sugar lingering in the wine (9 grams per litre, if you need to know), and this can leave the wine tasting rather austere.

U

Ugni Blanc – The most widely cultivated white grape variety of France and the mainstay of many a cheap dry white wine. To date it has been better known as the provider of base wine for distilling into armagnac and cognac, but lately the name has been appearing on wine labels. Technology seems to be improving the performance of the grape. The curious name is pronounced 'OON-yee', and is the same variety as Italy's ubiquitous Trebbiano.

Utiel-Requena – Region and *Denominación de Origen* of Mediterranean Spain inland from Valencia. Principally red wines from Bobal, Garnacha and Tempranillo grapes grown at relatively high altitude, between 600 and 900 metres.

V

Vacqueyras – Village of the southern Rhône Valley of France in the region better known for its generic appellation, the Côtes du Rhône. Vacqueyras can date its winemaking history all the way back to 1414, but has only been producing under its own village AC since 1991. The wines, from Grenache and Syrah grapes, can be wonderfully silky and intense, spicy and long-lived.

Valdepeñas – An island of quality production amidst the ocean of mediocrity that is Spain's La Mancha region – where most of the grapes are grown for distilling into the head-banging brandies of Jerez. Valdepeñas reds are made from a grape they call the Cencibel – which turns out to be a very close relation of the Tempranillo grape that is the mainstay of the fine but expensive red wines of Rioja. Again, like Rioja, Valdepeñas wines are matured in oak casks to give them a vanilla-rich smoothness. Among bargain reds, Valdepeñas is a name to look out for.

Valpolicella – Red wine of Verona, Italy. Good examples have ripe, cherry fruit and a pleasingly dry finish. Unfortunately, there are many bad examples of Valpolicella. Shop with circumspection. Valpolicella Classico wines, from the best vineyards clustered around the town, are more reliable. Those additionally labelled *superiore* have higher alcohol and some bottle age.

vanilla – Ageing wines in oak barrels (or, less picturesquely, adding oak chips to wine in huge concrete vats) imparts a range of characteristics including a smell of vanilla from the ethyl vanilline naturally given off by oak.

varietal – A varietal wine is one named after the grape variety (one or more) from which it is made. Nearly all everyday wines worldwide are now labelled in this way. It is salutary to contemplate that until the present wine boom began in the 1980s, wines described thus were virtually unknown outside Germany and one or two quirky regions of France and Italy.

vegan-friendly – My informal way of noting that a wine is claimed to have been made not only with animal-product-free finings (*see* vegetarian wine) but without any animal-related products whatsoever, such as livestock manure in the vineyards.

vegetal – A tasting note definitely open to interpretation. It suggests a smell or flavour reminiscent less of fruit (apple, pineapple, strawberry and the like) than of something leafy or even root based. Some wines are evocative (to some tastes) of beetroot, cabbage or even unlikelier vegetable flavours – and these characteristics may add materially to the attraction of the wine.

vegetarian wine – Wines labelled 'suitable for vegetarians' have been made without the assistance of animal products for 'fining' – clarifying – before bottling. Gelatine, egg whites, isinglass from fish bladders and casein from milk are among the items shunned, usually in favour of bentonite, an absorbent clay first found at Benton in the US state of Montana.

Verdejo – White grape of the Rueda region in north-west Spain. It can make superbly perfumed crisp dry whites of truly distinctive character and has helped make Rueda one of the best white-wine sources of Europe. No relation to Verdelho.

Verdelho – Portuguese grape variety once mainly used for a medium-dry style of Madeira, also called Verdelho, but now rare. The vine is now prospering in Australia, where it can make well-balanced dry whites with fleeting richness and lemon-lime acidity.

Verdicchio – White grape variety of Italy best known in the DOC zone of Castelli di Jesi in the Adriatic wine region of the Marches. Dry white wines once known for little more than their naff amphora-style bottles but now gaining a reputation for interesting, herbaceous flavours of recognisable character.

Vermentino – White grape variety principally of Italy, especially Sardinia. Makes florally scented soft dry whites.

Vieilles vignes – Old vines. Many French producers like to claim on their labels that the wine within is from vines of notable antiquity. While it's true that vines don't produce useful grapes for the first few years after planting, it is uncertain whether vines of much greater age – say 25 years plus – than others actually make better fruit. There are no regulations governing the use of the term, so it's not a reliable indicator anyway.

Vin de France – In effect, the new Vin de Table of France's morphing wine laws. The label may state the vintage (if all the wine in the blend does come from a single year's harvest) and the grape varieties that constitute the wine. It may not state the region of France from which the wine originates.

vin de liqueur – Sweet style of white wine mostly from the Pyrenean region of south-westernmost France, made by adding a little spirit to the new wine before it has fermented out, halting the fermentation and retaining sugar.

vin de pays – 'Country wine' of France. Introduced in 1968 and regularly revised ever since, it's the wine-quality designation between basic Vin de France and AOC/AOP. Although being superseded by the more recently introduced IGP (*qv*), there are more than 150 producing areas permitted to use the description vin de pays. Some vin de pays areas are huge: the Vin de Pays d'Oc (referencing the Languedoc region) covers much of the Midi and Provence. Plenty of wines bearing this humble designation are of astoundingly high quality and certainly compete with New World counterparts for interest and value. *See* Indication Géographique Protégée.

vin de table – Formerly official designation of generic French wine, now used only informally. *See* Vin de France.

vin doux naturel – Sweet, mildly fortified wine of southern France. A little spirit is added during the winemaking process, halting the fermentation by killing the yeast before it has consumed all the sugars – hence the pronounced sweetness of the wine.

vin gris – Rosé wine from Provence.

Vinho de mesa – 'Table wine' of Portugal.

Vino da tavola – The humblest official classification of Italian wine. Much ordinary plonk bears this designation, but the bizarre quirks of Italy's wine laws dictate that some of that country's finest wines are also classed as mere vino da tavola (table wine). If an expensive Italian wine is labelled as such, it doesn't mean it will be a disappointment.

Vino de la Tierra – Generic classification for regional wines, Spain. Abbreviates to VdT.

Vino de mesa – 'Table wine' of Spain. Usually very ordinary.

vintage – The grape harvest. The year displayed on bottle labels is the year of the harvest. Wines bearing no date have been blended from the harvests of two or more years.

Viognier – A white grape variety once exclusive to the northern Rhône Valley in France where it makes expensive Condrieu. Now, Viognier is grown more widely, in North and South America as well as elsewhere in France, and occasionally produces soft, marrowy whites that echo the grand style of Condrieu itself. The Viognier is now commonly blended with Shiraz in red winemaking in Australia and South Africa. It does not dilute the colour and is confidently believed by highly experienced winemakers to enhance the quality. Steve Webber, in charge of winemaking at the revered De Bortoli estates in the Yarra Valley region of Victoria, Australia, puts between two and five per cent Viognier in with some of his Shiraz wines. 'I think it's the perfume,' he told me. 'It gives some femininity to the wine.'

Viura – White grape variety of Rioja, Spain. Also widely grown elsewhere in Spain under the name Macabeo. Wines have a blossomy aroma and are dry, but sometimes soft at the expense of acidity.

Vouvray – AC of the Loire Valley, France, known for still and sparkling dry white wines and sweet, still whites from late-harvested grapes. The wines, all from Chenin Blanc grapes, have a unique capacity for unctuous softness combined with lively freshness – an effect best portrayed in the demi-sec (slightly sweet) wines, which can be delicious and keenly priced.

Vranac – Black grape variety of the Balkans known for dense colour and tangy-bitter edge to the flavour. Best enjoyed in situ.

W

weight – In an ideal world the weight of a wine is determined by the ripeness of the grapes from which it has been made. In some cases the weight is determined merely by the quantity of sugar added during the production process. A good, genuine wine described as having weight is one in which there is plenty of alcohol and 'extract' – colour and flavour from the grapes. Wine enthusiasts judge weight by swirling the wine in the glass and then examining the 'legs' or 'tears' left clinging to the inside of the glass after the contents have subsided. Alcohol gives these runlets a dense, glycerine-like condition, and if they cling for a long time, the wine is deemed to have weight – a very good thing in all honestly made wines.

Winzergenossenschaft – One of the many very lengthy and peculiar words regularly found on labels of German wines. This means a winemaking co-operative. Many excellent German wines are made by these associations of growers.

woody – A subjective tasting note. A faintly rank odour or flavour suggesting the wine has spent too long in cask.

X

Xarel-lo – One of the main grape varieties for cava, the sparkling wine of Spain.

Xinomavro – Black grape variety of Greece. It retains its acidity even in the very hot conditions that prevail in many Greek vineyards, where harvests tend to over-ripen and make cooked-tasting wines. Modern winemaking techniques are capable of making well-balanced wines from Xinomavro.

Y

Yecla – Town and DO wine region of eastern Spain, close to Alicante, making interesting, strong-flavoured red and white wines, often at bargain prices.

yellow – White wines are not white at all, but various shades of yellow – or, more poetically, gold. Some white wines with opulent richness even have a flavour I cannot resist calling yellow – reminiscent of butter.

Z

Zibibbo – Sicilian white grape variety synonymous with north African variety Muscat of Alexandria. Scantily employed in sweet winemaking, and occasionally for drier styles.

Zierfandler – Esoteric white grape of Thermenregion, Austria. Aromatic dry wines and rare late-harvest sweet wines.

Zinfandel – Black grape variety of California. Makes brambly reds, some of which can age very gracefully, and 'blush' whites – actually pink, because a little of the skin colour is allowed to leach into the must. The vine is also planted in Australia and South America. The Primitivo of southern Italy is said to be a related variety, but makes a very different kind of wine.

Zweigelt – Black grape of Austria making juicy red wines for drinking young. Some wines are aged in oak to make interesting, heftier long-keepers.

Index